WARFLOWER

A True Story of Family, Service, and Life in Alaska

ROBERT STARK

Disclaimer: Memory is a tricky thing. So while this memoir is based on my memories, perhaps my memories are different from your memories. As the events which took place in this book become more and more distant they become more and more muddled, so I apologize beforehand if anything doesn't line up with the way you remember it. I would love to compare notes. Many names have been changed. All dialogue was recreated. Thank you for reading.

ISBN: 979-8-9861780-0-4 (Paperback)
ISBN: 979-8-9861780-1-1 (Hardcover)
ISBN: 979-8-9861780-2-8 (Ebook)

Front cover image by Najdan Mancic
Book design by Najdan Mancic

The poem, "Look God" was written by my grandfather Donald Raymond Moore Sr., during his time in the Vietnam War.

First printing edition 2022.

For Mother:
Thank You for believing,
Rest in Peace.

The color of the mountain this afternoon
is tinged with nostalgia.
The terrible war flower
has left her footprints—
countless petals of separation and death
in white and violet.

— THICH NHAT HANH

The difficulty is not so much to escape death; the real
difficulty is to escape from doing wrong.

— SOCRATES

In a war, you don't necessarily hate the poor bastard
on the other side. You don't even know him, though
you may have a lot in common. You just go on
fighting because fighting has come to be the way you
live. The way your father and his father before him
lived, maybe. You don't think about the morality of it,
right and wrong, good and evil. You don't think at all;
you don't dare. It might unman you.

— TOM CLARKE

PART I

The sun was cool and my spirits high as wind blew my imagination from Italy to Iraq, from where I was to where I would be. The roar of aircraft on the runway was like Bering Sea waves crashing against boulders during a blizzard. It was so loud I could hardly think. I was one of a thousand soldiers packing my rucksack in a grassy field as fifteen C-17s taxied into position with enough fuel to fly to Iraq and back by breakfast. I was assigned to the tenth and final chalk, the one to be shot down if anti-aircraft weapons zeroed in. I was an eighteen-year-old airborne infantryman with grenades and mortar rounds overflowing from my ruck.

If only my family could see me now, I thought.

"Hey Stark, let me get a chew," said John Sullivan. Sully was from a blue-collar family in Fontana, California. He boasted of his state's revolutionary politics, and infamous bodybuilder, actor, and governor. He was five foot eight, a hundred and forty-five pounds with a crooked nose and a cauliflower ear from bare-knuckle boxing. At times he acted thirty, but he was much older than me at twenty-two.

"I'm about to jump to my fucking death here and all you want is chew," I said.

He sneered. His name was cut from the jump roster and he was rightly pissed.

"I gave you enough dip the past two weeks to last a normal person six months," he said. "And this is the first time I've asked."

"You're a damn liar," I said, although he was telling the truth. I was constantly quitting.

"Maybe I am a liar," he said, "but right now I'm just a guy without a chew."

We laughed as I ran my fingers over the plastic lid in my cargo pocket.

"You didn't pack any?" I said. "You fucking cherry."

"I packed five logs in my ruck," he said, shoving me. "But since command decided to send cooks, clerks, and pogues instead of SAW gunners—I accidentally left them in the barracks with my ruck." I shook my head and tossed him the can, he packed it without a pop. "I guess they don't think a SAW gunner is important during an invasion," he said. He carefully opened the can, fully aware of the strip of label I kept attached to the lid for good luck. He stuffed a plug into his lower lip, wiped his mouth of grains, and spit into a small pool forming between us before handing me back the can. I added more to my lip. I had known Sully for four months at that point; four months of spending everyday training followed by long nights partying. We were privates, we were brothers.

"You pack it like a girl, Sully," said Brammer, stuffing a 155 mm mortar in his ruck.

"Go sprinkle some chew on your food, Shammer," said Sully. We all laughed.

"Maybe I will," said Brammer. "Tomorrow morning on the drop zone."

"Fuck off," said Sully, shoving Brammer. "You bastard."

Brammer dipped so much it was a surprise he had teeth, which were relatively white and relatively straight. We called him Smeagol from Lord of the Rings, chew was his precious.

"Hey Stark," said Brammer. "If we die tonight, at least we will die with a dip in our lips."

I nodded.

"You guys are not going to die," said Sully. "We'll meet up in a couple of days. You'll see."

"What if we do?" I said. "What then?"

"You better have lived," said Brammer. "Because we are nothing but *hajji* worm food after that."

"There has to be more than this," I said. "It can't be the end, maybe just the beginning."

Brammer laughed, "You are a stinking hippie, Stark. What you see is what you get."

I shook my head, "Just because I believe in an afterlife doesn't make me a hippie."

Sully patted my shoulder. "I am from California, I know hippies, and you are definitely a hippie."

They laughed.

"Fuck off." I cinched down the straps of my ruck and tucked them in.

"It's okay," said Sully. "Brothers are always different. You, Stark, are the hippie, Brammer is pure white trash and I'm an intellectual who should be on the cover of Men's Health Magazine."

We nodded, laughed, and spit in the pool while the rhythm of a thousand men cleaning rifles, packing rucksacks, and preparing for battle happened all around. It was the scariest, most beautiful moment of my life up to that point. I stared at the row of planes and watched grass blow in the breeze.

"Are you guys ready for this?" said Brammer.

"For what?" I asked.

"War," he said. We sat in silence for a second and thought. "They can call it whatever the fuck they want, but in the end—it's all the same. We're going to war."

"I'm as ready as ever," I said, keeping my shaky hands moving by field stripping my rifle.

Sullivan nodded and clenched his jaw.

"Let's kill them before they kill us," said Brammer, oiling his squad automatic weapon.

"I'll fight to the death for you guys," said Sully. "If they let me."

"You'll have your chance," said Brammer. "Don't stress about things you can't control."

"You guys are closer to me than my own brother," I said. "I'll do whatever it takes to for us to get home in one piece."

"Don't get all sappy on us," said Brammer, patting my shoulder, "you stinking hippie."

We laughed as I shook my head and spit. I used a folded paper towel from my back pocket to wipe sweat from my brow. For some reason, I always carried one. I stared at the final aircraft, the one I would be loading up on, and wondered—In a few hours I will be in that plane flying toward Iraq. At least we will only be gone for a couple of weeks. What the fuck is going to happen? If I die, will I go to heaven, or will I be reincarnated?

"I can't believe this shit!" said Sully. "They cut a fucking SAW gunner from an infantry squad instead of a cook. What, are they going to fry some fucking bacon on the drop zone?"

"They probably don't even know how," said Brammer. "Army cooks can't cook for shit."

I laughed, trying to make sense of things was pointless and potentially harmful.

"Maybe you'll be glad you didn't jump," I said. "In case we die. You could tell the world what a shitbag Jerry Brammer was."

We laughed as Brammer shoved me and grabbed me behind the neck trying to start a grappling match. I broke free and stood back, I've always been more of a pacifist than a fighter.

"I'd rather die with you guys tonight than live the rest of my life knowing I should have," said Sully.

We nodded. My skin was covered in goosebumps, I was cold and afraid. If only my family could see me now, I thought.

"The recruiter didn't lie when he said I'd travel," I said. "I just didn't think it'd be like this." Brammer patted my shoulder and clenched his jaw. He was twenty-three; two years older than my big brother, Brammer was the elder of our trio. After acing the entrance exam, he was offered any job the army had, but since he had fired his first machine gun at ten and knew more about weaponry than the master gunners, he traded an athletic scholarship to Duke for a blue cord and maroon beret. Infantry all the way.

Large speakers started blasting Outkast's "Bombs Over Baghdad" and soldiers began cheering and hollering. Bombs dropped on Baghdad while we prepared in Italy. Americans watched the news at home and prayed to Jesus. Iraqis watched the news at home and prayed to Mohammed. Private Brian, a white kid from Cleveland, started doing the crip walk while the black guys and Hispanics cheered him on.

Brammer shook his head, "Fucking wigger."

Sully and I shook our heads at his comment.

The song ended and somebody announced "Formation" over the speakers and the word was echoed by a thousand paratroopers shuffling towards the podium.

"Great," whispered Brammer. "I can't wait to hear this."

"Maybe he'll tell us why SAW gunners were cut," said Sully.

"Hurry the fuck up," yelled our team leader, Sergeant Debaser. "When a colonel gives a speech, you fucking double time." Everybody moved at the same speed as before.

Lieutenant Colonel Tunnell was an American of Nephilim proportions. Educated at Purdue and West Point—he had a baritone voice, muscular frame, and willingness to lead from the front. If there was ever a worthy man to follow, he was it.

"Red Devils!" He hollered and raised a large black fist. We roared like thunder. We raised our fists, a thousand colors united under one flag. He continued, "We are doing for our country what millions of Americans have done before. We are taking the fight to the enemy. Saddam and his Regime have persecuted the Kurdish and Iraqi people for too long. It is genocide and we will stop it. The time has come to end his lawless disregard of humanity, and to take him down before attacks like 9/11 become nightly news."

I replayed the news flashes of the towers being struck by airplanes and Americans jumping out of windows to their death. Firefighters carrying burn victims, searching through the rubble while everybody crying. The song, "Where Were You When The World Stopped Turning" played in my head, and I knew that my favorite country singer would be proud of me.

"Tonight," he continued, "while your friends are drinking on a bar stool at home watching the nightly news, you will be making history. We will win this war! Not only are we tougher, faster, and better trained, but we are fighting for what is right." We nodded our heads. "I will be the first man on the ground," he said, "and I will fight beside each of you until I die a warrior's death."

He stood strong like a Viking, locking eyes with every soldier before raising his fist.

"Red Devils!" he yelled. "Follow me!"

We roared like Spartans as "Bombs over Baghdad" came on the speakers, and ordinary life became a movie.

We loaded in buses that brought us to a dining facility for prime rib, lobster, and the works. We ate like it was the last supper. I was too young to die. After the meal, we laid on cots in an empty hangar that smelled like sweaty feet and ball sweat before returning to our rucks. Sully stayed behind.

It was colder, darker, and scarier than before.

"You ready?" Brammer patted my shoulder. I shrugged, grateful it was too dark for him to see my face. "Let's put our chutes on and get this party started."

Parachutes are issued by size, I am a size three, and so is Brammer. We took turns strapping each other in.

"I wonder how long we'll be there?" I asked, trying to think quietly.

"Until the mission is complete," he said.

"What mission?"

"To kill Saddam and take down the Republican Guard." He tightened the shoulder straps as I winced. "Nobody knows how long it will take, so don't think about it. Let's complete the first mission and take it from there."

I nodded and raised my arms for the reserve. I put on Brammer's chute after he was done with mine. Burning in my lip was chew, burning in my heart was fear. It was the first time I felt like puking because I was so scared. My body shook uncontrollably. I tried to convince myself that I was keeping America safe but couldn't forget the millions of Americans who died in similar missions. Some guys put their faith in Jesus, others put their faith in Buddha, my faith was in my comrades. When it was not enough, I tried prayer.

"Okay, God," I whispered, "it's you and me." I spit. "Make sure I don't get shot out of the fucking sky, please. And watch over me while I'm gone. I swear to make something of my life when I return." I awkwardly made the cross and felt a hint of relief.

We hung our hundred-plus pound rucksacks and were inspected by a jumpmaster. Soldiers waddled to each other with rucks pounding knees. I could barely see their faces, but nobody looked scared. "Keep your feet and knees together," they said, or "see you downrange." I didn't understand why everybody called the place "downrange," but I didn't ask. I was the youngest person there and I sure as shit didn't want anybody to know I was afraid. Nobody mentioned enemy or death. I shivered like I was back home in Alaska only it wasn't because of the cold weather. Sully returned just as we were about to load up.

"I wish I could be with you guys, tonight," he said. "This is such bullshit."

"We'll see you in a few days," said Brammer. "Don't worry about it."

"Remember—jump as far as you can," he said. "And keep your feet and knees together." He surprised us with a two-armed hug. "You are my only brothers, so don't fucking die on me."

"Don't get all emo on us," said Brammer. "It's not the time. Remember—bring a bunch of Copenhagen, we'll be out by the time you get there."

"Roger," said Sully, sniffling. "I'll see you guys in a few days."

He patted our reserves, spit at our boots, and joined the formation of sulking soldiers scratched from the jump. I felt for them. We would earn a gold star known as a "mustard stain" on our airborne wings to show we jumped into combat, they would not. I struggled to stand straight with the weight of my ruck yanking me down. Grateful to have been transformed from an alcoholic, pill snorting seventeen-year-old to a strong, able-bodied eighteen-year-old in a matter of months. I felt like a man. A light rain began to fall as sweat ran down my hairless chest, to my privates, and down my legs. Airplane engines revved and it smelled like jet fuel and fresh rain.

"This is it!" I shouted to Brammer. "Here we go!"

"Our entire lives led to this moment," he hollered. "Remember—chamber a round when you hit the ground then get your night vision ready." I nodded. "See you at the assembly area." We patted shoulders, clenched jaws, and shuffled to our separate chalks. I wondered if I would ever see him again.

I waited in line for a final inspection at the tail end of the aircraft with my hands on my helmet and back flexed. The jumpmasters inspected every chute and reserve. The weight of the ruck, tightness of the parachute straps, and pain of the rifle digging into my hip were almost unbearable. Not to mention the stream of sweat running from my helmet to my boots. Hot wind from the props blasted my face, yet still, I shivered. I was ready to be in the fucking desert. I stared at an American flag hanging inside the plane wondering what was happening back home. The cheering had long ceased, the only sounds were my thumping heart and roaring engines.

After inspections, we waddled up the gangway to squeeze into narrow webbed seats with our rucks on our laps. A sigh of relief was echoed. An old woman with brown paper bags full of snacks and thank you cards from elementary schoolchildren said she would pray for us and then walked out. I hid my eyes. The ramp raised and doors closed, land disappeared.

Silence.

If fear has a taste, it is a combination of shellfish, ball sweat, and Copenhagen. Please—don't tell anybody—I was so scared I thought I was going to shit my pants.

As the plane began movement and lifted from the runway, we hollered like Vikings, Spartans, Americans—until leveling off at cruising altitude. All eyes went inward. Soldiers snacked, dipped, prayed. Lights turned off, everything became dark and cold. I still shivered yet stopped sweating.

I visualized my mother on the phone with her husband in

prison. I saw my brother pacing alone in a solitary confinement cell. Where was our father? What was he like? Would I ever hear his voice or meet him? I imagined my friends in Seward huddled around a bonfire on the beach drinking cheap vodka and laughing. Northern lights danced between peaks on a canvas of stars. They whistled to the spirits in hopes of being carried away to the land of lights. A meteor shot across the sky and they watched it until its tail burned out. They made a wish. Elliot, my sweetheart, wished for my return. I know she did. Elliot loved me when nobody else did. When my mother chose to love a murderer over me, and father chose to love nobody over me, and my brother chose to be the leader of a prison gang over me, Elliot loved me. Will she love me if I return, or remember me if I die? Will she remember the time we made a bed on her mother's living room floor and stayed naked for two days as snow fell outside the sliding glass door and VHS movies replayed on the television? I thought about Benny Benson, the Alaskan orphan who designed our state flag and was reminded that we can all do great things despite our backgrounds. I saw my history teacher's face when he kicked me out of the class senior year after I called him out for picking on students; I was making history while he was teaching it, the fuck stick. I recalled the first naked woman I ever saw when I was in fifth grade and my friend's mother changed out of lacy white underwear and stood naked staring at the blanket I hid under on the couch.

A jumpmaster shouted something I could not understand, breaking my concentration. It was pitch black and freezing, my heart pounded. Red lights came on above the doors and white lights in the walkway.

"Stand up, hook up!" The jumpmasters yelled from both doors.

Had we just taken off? I wondered. Had I been asleep? Was I dreaming? Holy shit!

I grunted and stood like everybody else with my left hand covering the reserve and right hand holding the static line attached to a cable overhead. I shook and listened to boots shuffle and people whisper the Lord's Prayer.

"Check equipment!"

I checked every strap and buckle from chin to groin before the guy behind me slapped my ass and yelled, "Okay!" I smacked the guy's ass in front of me and it was passed forward until the jumper in the door held his hand straight in front of the jumpmaster and yelled, "All okay jumpmaster," and the jumpmaster smacked his hand and waited.

The doors opened and cold air rushed in. I was too far back to see outside but I could certainly feel it, and it was certainly not hot desert air. I shuffled forward, unaware of anything else on the planet. I had never been so present. If fear has a smell, it smells like Doritos, ball sweat, and Copenhagen. The plane nose-dived from cruising altitude to five hundred feet and our rucks became weightless. I stretched my back like everybody else, seconds turned into hours. The moment we leveled out, the red lights above the doors turned green and the jumpmasters yelled, "Go, go, go!" Guys in front were swept out the door as I shuffled forward listening for gunfire. I slammed the riser in the jumpmaster's hand, turned ninety degrees, and tried to jump. But since my ruck was so damn heavy, I fell forward into pitch-black darkness, thankful not to hit the side of the plane.

I dropped so fast that I barely had time to struggle to keep my feet and knees together. I could not see the ground, so I had no idea when or where I would land. A single light in the distance terrified me; *hajji* was waiting to kill me. I landed in knee-deep mud without injury. Everything was soaked, but I was alive! I laid on my back, cut the tangled risers, removed the parachute harness, took my rifle out of the case, and loaded a round.

Here we go, I thought. Let's do this right, let's kill these bastards in the middle of the night.

I attached the night vision goggles to my helmet and made sure the carabiner was attached to the band. Two pick-up trucks without lights and a handful of soldiers were on the runway. My trigger finger shook outside the housing as I watched them. I assumed they were friendlies because nobody fired, so I continued to scan the muddy valley, surprised to be surrounded by rolling mountains and a nearby village. Hundreds of soldiers struggled to stand with their waterlogged rucks, others trudged slowly towards the runway. One soldier tried to lift his ruck over his head but couldn't because of the weight, so he grabbed a shoulder strap with both hands to swing it onto his back but lost balance and fell. He kicked the ruck, squatted with his lower back pressed against the hip belt, tightened the shoulder straps, and planted his feet to rock forward. As he stood and took a step, his boots became stuck and he fell forward trying to yank them out, punching the mud. Dozens fell with their feet stuck. The rain had been in the forecast, but nobody expected knee-deep mud.

It was my turn.

I pulled out the compass and shot a bearing to the northeast corner of the runway, towards my platoon's assembly area. Unwilling to pack my parachute into the aviator kit bag, I left it for whoever took Sully's place to collect in the morning, and using the back against hip belt/rocking technique, I surprisingly stood and began walking towards solid ground. Perhaps thirteen years of skateboarding and snowboarding were finally paying off. I had balance.

My boots sank over the top laces with every step. When I pulled one up to move forward, the transfer of weight drove the other one deeper. I struggled in slow motion, reminded of post-holing up snowy mountains with a snowboard in my arms and a backpack on my shoulders. I took my time. I passed soldiers lying behind their rucks where they stayed all night, many were frostbitten by morning. Grunts and grimaces echoed across the valley due to broken legs, broken backs, and other lesser injuries.

I walked beside two soldiers before they both lost their

balance and fell. They asked for help but I refused. I did not recognize their voices and could not carry their weight. I firmly believe in the power of momentum. A soldier approached on the south edge of the runway and startled me by shouting.

"Who you with, soldier?" he said.

"173rd Airborne Brigade," I said, quietly. "1/508th, Alpha Company Second Platoon."

"Speak up," he shouted. "And it's sergeant."

I walked past him as he yelled at my back. At the northeast corner of the runway, I pulled out my compass to recheck the azimuth. I noticed two soldiers holding a fluorescent panel with infrared chem-lights arranged as my operation order explained. When I was within a few feet, my platoon sergeant whispered in his squeaky voice.

"Who you with, soldier?"

"It's Stark, sergeant," I said. "Private Stark."

"I'll be damned," he said. "Golden Child—you quick, kid. Not as quick as me, though."

"Roger sergeant."

"Follow Corporal Corn," he said. "He'll put you in position."

"Roger sergeant."

Corn tapped my shoulder and pointed toward our invisible platoon before walking away at a near sprint, seemingly unaware of my heavy ass rucksack and minimal night vision training. I tried to keep pace but fell behind, almost tripping multiple times in deep depressions. Depth perception is nearly non-existent with NVGs. The moon and stars were hiding, all was dark besides a single terrifying light from the village. I finally noticed a dozen soldiers on their bellies in a large circle and realized that it was my platoon. I had completed the first mission, and I wondered about Brammer. Lieutenant Spencer knelt in the center of the circle whispering on the radio as his radio telephone operator lay a few feet away pulling security. Corn waited until the LT was finished then directed me into position at six o'clock with Specialist Reed.

I removed my ruck, put it in front of me then laid in a puddle that covered my torso, back, and entire lower body. Everything but my head and neck were submerged. Corn assigned me a sector of fire before racing back to the platoon sergeant. I was colder and shakier than before. Scared and relieved at the same time.

"You awake?" I whispered.

"My dick is going to freeze off," he said, with a thick Jersey accent. It was hard to understand him because he spoke so fast. "In fucking Iraq of all places."

"No, it won't," I snickered. "You heard about Brammer?" I asked. As a team leader, Reed had a handheld radio and knew what was going on.

"Nah," he said. "But since you're a private, put your poncho over this puddle so we can get out of the mud."

I didn't think it would work, but I was trained to follow orders. So with shaky hands, I removed the poncho from the outside middle pouch, and as Reed rolled on his side I laid it over the puddle. When he rolled back, he sank into the water, and we were back in the same fucking puddle, only now my poncho was muddy.

"I swear to God my fucking dick is going to freeze off." He said, trying to get closer. "I can't feel it, man, I really can't."

"Your dick is not going to freeze off," I said, shoving him. "Quit worrying about it. I can't feel mine either."

"Really?" He said. "Don't fucking lie to me, Stark. I ain't got no kids, man. I would rather go home missing legs than missing my dick."

"The sun will rise in the morning and your dick will thaw out," I said. "Just calm down."

"I hope you're fucking right," he said, breathing heavy.

I scanned my sector while trying to resist thoughts. I wished I was in a warm bed with Elliot instead of a cold puddle with a guy I hardly knew. I searched my pockets for a can of chew but found only wet flakes, plastic shards, and mud. The can exploded on impact. I dug through my ruck and found two rolls in the same condition.

"Fuck," I whispered, I wanted to yell.

"Sup?"

"My cans broke."

"You should've packed them better."

"No shit."

"Give me a chew anyway."

I took a pinch of muddy chew mixed with plastic pieces and my burning lip revived me. Reed did the same. We kicked each other for hours to stay awake. I realized that being a real-life soldier is nothing like playing a video game. After hours of trembling, sunlight arrived with a hint of warmth, exposing barren mountains and the nearby village. Hundreds of soldiers squirmed on their bellies and backs in the mud trying to pack away their night vision. I didn't understand why we hadn't destroyed the village; I didn't understand the difference between Kurds, Sunnis, and Shias; I knew one word, *hajji*. The muddy field glimmered as I removed my night vision from my helmet, packed them into my ruck, and locked eyes with Brammer. We held up our dirty fists, clenched our jaws, and nodded. Our platoon sergeant and LT spoke for a few minutes as we waited in silence.

"Smoke 'em if you got 'em," said the platoon sergeant. "We're moving out, so pack your shit."

Reed lit a cigarette and I bummed one. Everybody smoked. We struggled to lift our rucks, even with help, especially one of my teammates, Private Loveall.

I had assumed that Loveall's first experience with physical labor was in basic training, where they waived his failed physical fitness tests because we needed numbers. He was six feet three inches tall and weighed a hundred and forty-five pounds soaking wet. Pale and frail with gangly teeth and pink eyes, he reminded me of a terrified snowshoe hare. He tried to stand with his ruck but his shaky knees buckled and he collapsed into the mud. He rolled around on his back and belly until his entire body was covered in mud while sergeants laughed and mocked him. I thought he would drown, but I didn't say anything—because I was the youngest and lowest ranking and I didn't want people to think that I was some kind of a softy. His slow blinking eyes stared at the pale blue sky and he mumbled incoherently.

"Loveall, you fucking wimp," yelled Debaser. "Stand up."

"Get up, weakling," shouted Corn.

"You're a pathetic excuse of a soldier," said our squad leader, sergeant Hollywood.

"I'm sorry, sergeant," whispered Loveall, "but I can't."

"Stand up," yelled Debaser. "You fucking pussy!"

"I can't," he said. "I just can't." Tears ran down his cheeks.

Our platoon sergeant shook his head in disbelief. "Sergeant Debaser," he said. "You and Golden Child stay behind and help him."

"Roger, sergeant."

"Second platoon," he held his arms straight behind him. "Form a wedge." Forty or so mud-covered soldiers moved into a staggered wedge with lit cigarettes dangling from dirty lips. "Follow me," he said, waving his left arm over his head. Everybody moved out.

Suddenly it was only Debaser, Loveall, and I, and I became terrified of being overrun by people from the village. Debaser continued yelling at Loveall; he made him look bad as a leader, he said. All Loveall could do was whisper apologies from a spread eagle position in the mud. No matter what was said, the poor bastard could not stand. I wished Debaser would just stop yelling.

"He can't carry his gear," said Debaser. "Let's grab his ruck with one hand on the frame and move until we need a break."

"Roger," I said.

"He can carry the rifle and AT-4," he said. "Can you handle that, Loveall?"

"Roger sergeant," he said. Mumbling with mud in his teeth, mud on his face, and mud on his eyelids.

Debaser and I took small, fast steps resting often. Loveall could hardly place a boot in front of the other without losing balance and falling over. I became furious. I told him that he should have stayed home or been a pogue because I was carrying his rucksack while Sully was stuck in Italy. It got to a point where he claimed he couldn't even walk, so we left him behind about fifty meters and waited. I had never seen a more pathetic and desperate person. We walked back to him, leaving his ruck in the mud. He was lying on his back staring at the sky with empty eyes.

"I can't do it," he said. "I can't go on."

Debaser was too angry to speak, he shook his head.

"Quit being a fucking pussy," I said, spitting on his boots. "Get the fuck up!"

He could barely stand, and when he did he swayed like a tall tree in heavy wind. His glazed eyes moved from Debaser's to mine, Debaser's to mine, Debaser's to mine, before flicking the selector switch on his rifle from safe to semi and spinning it until the barrel pointed at his open mouth. I froze. It still haunts me that I froze. His eyes closed and his face winced as he slowly put pressure on the trigger. Debaser smacked the barrel out of his face and shoved him back into the mud.

"You fucking idiot," he yelled. "You're too fucking young

to die! Give me the fucking AT-4." Debaser handed me the rifle and grabbed the rocket launcher.

"You're a real bitch," I said. "We just got here!"

Loveall could barely lift his helmet out of the mud to look at us. We walked away and he followed. We continued to stop and wait for him. After we reached our platoon at the road, I washed my hands and face and rifles in a mud puddle. Iraqi men with kind eyes and weathered faces gave us warm chapatis from a straw basket and hot chai. I was afraid of them until Brammer explained they were Kurdish and the entire reason we arrived. I was grateful for their company then and came to respect and appreciate the men in white turbans. I was happy that it was not raining, I was not shaking, and they were not trying to kill us. I learned to count my blessings. Debaser told the LT and platoon sergeant about the incident, I told Brammer, and the next day the Chaplain came to talk with Loveall and take him away to someplace warm, peaceful, and full of pretty women and tasty food, or so I imagined. It was the last time I saw Loveall outside of a dream, though I often wonder if his rifle would have even fired?

On my mother's side of the family, every male served in the military. On my father's side of the family, every male served prison time. My brother went to prison and I joined the army, we pride ourselves on family traditions. Mother used to comment on how handsome a man is in uniform, and I believed her. Her first husband was a golden gloves boxer in prison, her second husband was a Major in the National Guard, and her third and final husband was a murderer doing life without parole. Mother loved a man in uniform. She did her best for her two sons, and now she and my father are both dead, which is why I can finally tell this story.

The birth of my bad eardrums was on July 17, 1984, in Caldwell, Idaho. We stayed there for a couple of weeks before moving to California in a Jayco trailer so dad could work on oil rigs. The pictures of them together are priceless because there are so few. They looked happy, free, madly in love, and young. I have a picture of my smiling mother seated on a lawn chair behind the trailer with me in her arms and James in a pack and play. She looks excited, adventurous, courageous, and beautiful. Our father is in the background smoking a cigarette in a tank-top that shows his cut-up body.

Mother wanted him to quit drinking and drugging and to come home after work to help out instead of going to the bar, but he wasn't having it. James had been sick and crying for a week, and since I have always been a cry baby, I added tears to the tension. Mother needed a break. So she stormed to the bar with two boys on her hip trying to drag him out. He refused to leave, mother persisted. He smacked her across the face so hard she fell next to the pool table. We fell, too, and continued to bawl. Two men tackled him and beat him up. Mother loaded us into the truck and began the long drive north to Idaho, leaving Bert behind. I didn't see his face or hear his voice for twenty-five years. It wasn't the first time he hit her, but it was the last. We stayed for a couple of weeks with family in Idaho, until our uncle in Nome, Alaska bought his kid sister a plane ticket to move our family north to a remote town north of the arctic circle. He had a son and daughter with a Korean woman he met and married while stationed in Korea. After a week of being in Nome, his wife left for Korea and never returned. My mother would take care of the housework and kids while her brother paid the bills.

My memories of those early years in Uncle Don's house include: riding a sled down the stairs inside the house, peeing in a trash can in the bathroom, lighting the carpet on fire with my brother, consistently falling asleep at the dinner table because I was so tired from playing, building snow forts in the yard with snow that was deeper than my head, and catching salmon on the beach with a rod and reel. They were great years, playful years. I was outside every season, rain, snow, or sunshine. Mother's technique for raising kids was to keep them playing outside as much as possible, and it worked.

After several years, mother met a Major in the National Guard named Dan Silver who promised to provide a house, food, and security. They were married on May 2, 1989, and slow danced to "Love Can Build a Bridge" by The Judds. I love The Judds. Dan was a Shriner, Mason, and Rotary Club member who played rhythm guitar and sang in a band. He didn't smile very often unless he was on stage; he loved being on stage and my mother loved to dance with us boys while he played. I often wished he stayed on stage. He wasn't a bad father. As years have passed, I can honestly say he was a pretty typical American father for the time. He worked, paid no attention to the kids, watched hours of television every day, and rarely showed emotions other than anger. We visited his parents in Missouri where I realized that he smiled way more than they did. Dan was rarely home, and when he was, he watched Star Trek, Babylon 5, and Stargate SG1, both new episodes, and re-runs. Mother recorded every show he missed on VHS; I still hate the fucking Sci-Fi Channel.

James, mother and I were in the process of moving from Uncle Don's home into Dan's house. We carried boxes full of our belongings from a red Ford Bronco, one of the older, smaller, cooler ones, across a big deck into the front door.

I set a box down in the living room and then stopped to recon my surroundings.

"Are you going to get outside and grab something or let your mother do all the work?" said mother, coming inside through the front door. She had a big perm, big glasses, and a big box in her hands.

"I want to look around," I said. "Where is my room?"

"Get outside and grab something or I'll kick your butt," said James. My brother was three years older, much bigger, and loved to remind me of it.

"You'll have plenty of time to explore when we get everything inside," she said.

"I don't want to," I said. "I'm tired."

"You better, little brother," James dropped the box and clenched his fists, "or else."

"Now boys," said Mother, "it's not time for roughhousing."

I ran outside to the deck and heard Bering Sea waves crashing against boulders. I watched them only two blocks away and stared out at the open water. I looked down the stairs at the Bronco, loaded above the windows and parked beside a rusty shipping container, and sprinted into the nearby field to hide on my belly next to a pond. James shouted my name and I acted deaf.

"Why does Robert get to play all the time and I have to work?"

"Because he is five and you are eight," said mother. "You are the older brother, so you need to take care of him."

"That's not fair," he said. "I'll take care of him all right."

"Life is not fair," she said. "Where is he?"

"Over there," he pointed in my direction.

"Robert," she called. "Come and help, honey, we are almost done."

I played deaf until she started the countdown.

"One," I held my ground. "Two," I moved into a crouch. "Thr…" I jumped up and ran toward them.

"I'm coming," I said. "I'm coming!"

I explained that I was lured by a leprechaun to the pond and they shook their heads. I grabbed the smallest box then walked up the stairs across the deck in the front door and set the box on the couch. A glass bowl full of shiny, green rectangles resembled a delicious candy I had never seen. I loved candy, so I picked one up for closer inspection.

"Andes," it read. I had never heard of Andes, but it smelled like mint chocolate, my favorite. I made sure the coast was clear before carefully removing the wrapper. A chocolate rectangle with a thin green line dividing the top and bottom. It looked perfect. I closed my eyes and took a tiny bite of a corner just as Dan walked in with sweat running down his face and a large box in his hands. I shoved the entire thing in my mouth. He slammed the box on the dinner table and stared. I stood still. I didn't know whether to laugh and smile and tell him I had eaten candy and that it was delicious, or to be afraid, and based on the seriousness of his face I was afraid. Would he make a big deal out of a piece of candy? I wondered. Mother would never marry somebody like that.

"What are you doing in here, Robert?" Said James, dropping a box on the ground. "Get outside and help." I sprinted outside in fear.

"Sheri," Dan said, standing on the deck, "get inside." He pointed at the door, "Now."

Mother inhaled and spoke calmly. "How about we finish unloading first, sweetheart?"

"I need to talk to you," he said. His pale face was blotchy, "Now."

I was scared. The door slammed behind her and he began yelling. James and I snuck on the deck where we could see our mother crying on the linoleum floor as he stood over her with a belt. We ran to the field to scoop beetles out of the pond.

"What'd you do this time?" James asked.

"I ate a piece of candy from a bowl inside," I said.

"You stole from Dan," he said, grinning. "Nice work little brother." He patted my shoulder.

"I didn't steal," I said. "I just ate a piece of candy."

"My little brother," he said. "A candy thief; I'm proud of you. I didn't know you had it in you."

Mother stepped outside and called our names. We ran to her. She wiped tears from her face with downcast eyes.

"Dan wants to know which one of you stole from him?"

"Is this about some stupid candy?" said James. "Let's move back to Uncle Don's! Dan is an asshole."

"Dan counts his mints every night," she said, "and there is one less than last night. So, he wants to know, who stole from him?" She bit her trembling lip and waited. My eyes were weighed down with guilt and fear. "One of you boys is going to 'fess up," she said. "Or you will both be punished."

"I did it," said James. "I stole the fat fuck's candy."

"Is your brother telling the truth?" she looked at me with her hands on her hips.

"I didn't think it was a big deal," said James. "It's only a god damn mint. Besides, he shouldn't be eating candy anyway." He laughed. "The fat shit."

Dan stepped on the deck with a red face, furious eyes, and pointy nose.

"This is my god damn house," he said, pointing at us and walking down the stairs with a belt in his hand. "You little punks! Everything inside of this house is mine." He put his finger in our faces. "You god damn kids better not touch anything in this house, or you will pay for it. Is that clear?" James and I stood shoulder to shoulder. "Is that clear?"

"Say, 'Yes sir,' boys," said mother, wiping her eyes with a folded paper towel.

Dan's nostrils flared as he lifted the belt.

"Yes, sir," I said, biting my trembling lip.

"Yeah, sure," said James, smirking. Dan smacked him in the face and James stopped smiling.

"Sheri, you need to do something about what happened here," he said. "I refuse to have disrespectful runts in my house. Here," he handed her the belt, "take my belt and whoop 'em." Mother said nothing. She held the belt in her shaky hand and searched his narrow eyes for compassion. I trembled, James raised his chin.

She led us to the bedroom and told us to wait. A couple of minutes later she entered with her head down and belt dragging. We pulled our pants down and leaned over the bed. I cried, confessed, and begged her not to spank me.

"I'll never touch anything again, ma," I said, "I promise."

"Oh, Robert," she said, crying. "I know you won't, son. That's what I'm afraid of."

I had another uncle in Nome, not by blood, who was a librarian, a substitute teacher, and Santa Claus every Christmas. Everybody called him Railroad Joe, and I didn't know why. He was a single father with a house in town where James and I used to stay on weekends to play with his son and give our mother a break. Joe built monkey bars in his son's room that connected multiple nests furnished with pads and pillows where we slept. He acquired a crashed cargo plane, removed the tail from the fuselage, and attached it to the arctic entryway where he strung Christmas lights from the front door to the cockpit that was constantly lit. His son—Arlo, James, and I spent hours flying imaginary missions resupplying people in need. Some needed medicine, others needed gasoline; some needed food and others needed entertainment. Everybody needed love and affection. Joe let us run free, often joining our imaginary wanderings as co-pilot, flight attendant, or even hungry widow. He was bold enough to be goofy.

On Saturday and Sunday mornings, after we climbed down the ladder from our nest, we cuddled together with pillows and blankets on his wooden platform in the living room as he read Mark Twain or The Bible. He would be on his knees with a blanket covering his legs and a shoe on each knee cap, appearing as a dwarf. We listened with wide-open eyes on certain mornings and fell asleep on others. He never scolded us for sleeping or forced us to stay awake, he just kept on reading. Uncle Joe did not have a television. We made sourdough pancakes that looked like Mickey Mouse with chocolate chips, M&Ms or Teddy Grahams and we only ate after saying grace. We used to visit him at the library and help him shelve books. If we were reading, we didn't have to help. Joe taught me to love books.

He brought me ptarmigan hunting once, it was the only time I went hunting before Iraq. We watched a family of birds graze on low bush cranberries. Instead of shooting them, we watched them. Joe whispered about a universal spirit that exists in all of us. It travels from being to being without an identifiable source or destination. He spoke of the ptarmigan's need for family, food, and shelter, and how all it wanted was to be safe with the ones it loved. He aimed the shotgun at the sky and fired, causing the birds to fly and land a few feet away. They continued to graze as if nothing had happened.

"Chaos happens," he said, "it is the way of the Cosmos. How we deal with the chaos determines everything."

We harvested a gallon of berries before going home.

Weeks later he brought me to a wide-open valley of purple and green tundra inside rolling hills where thousands of caribou grazed and moved like a flock of birds in the sky. We laid on our bellies for hours in silent admiration. On the drive home, he asked what I thought of the caribou and the Cosmos. After a long pause, the only word that came to mind was "magic."

"Yes, Robert," he nodded and laughed. "I certainly believe in magic."

Weeks later he brought two beautiful women and a canoe to a small lake near the ocean where he put me in the canoe with a life jacket and made sure I was comfortable before letting me paddle to the middle of the lake. He said he would be back soon and not to worry. I trusted him. I listened to waves crash and wind blow beach grass as clouds passed overhead. The adults were out of sight until suddenly they ran naked to the ocean where they dove in laughing and screaming in joy. I did not see them for some time, which did not matter, because I trusted Joe.   I never saw Joe drink alcohol or smoke anything. He was the only adult I knew who didn't use either. He showed me that using intoxicants isn't necessary to be an adult, although it may seem like it. And that you don't have to be gruff, rude, and apathetic to be a man. Joe showed me a side of masculinity and humanity that I packed in my rucksack at a young age to carry with me through life.

41

When I was in first grade, my mother started driving the short bus. She worked with kids with developmental disabilities, and I used to visit her classroom to play with them. Mother was always smiling and laughing at work, even when they pooped their pants and she had to clean it up.

"I know it was a mistake," she said. "We all make mistakes. Lord knows I have."

She treated them the same way she treated all kids like they understood.

Marlena was my mother's favorite. She had multiple sclerosis so bad she was a tiny human. Her glasses were thick and her hair was short and black and she always wore a red bow. I wondered how such a tiny person hadn't been blown away by such fierce storms. Her legs were thin like seaweed, and she used crutches with supports to balance. I couldn't understand why such a young girl was in such bad shape, I still can't. Some things aren't meant to be understood. She was sweet, gentle, funny, and brave. When doctors told her to use a wheelchair, she refused. When kids teased her about her glasses, she said she could see through their meanness. I loved sitting with her and looking at her while trying to read her mind. She loved looking at me and making faces. We didn't talk much, we just stared like interested beings trying to figure out the mysteries of life, before making funny faces and laughing. Marlena talked to my mother more than she talked to anybody, which made her parents quite jealous.

The phone rang one morning as I was watching Tom and Jerry. Mother was frying bacon and eggs. No matter how hard Tom tried to get Jerry, he could not capture him. Mother answered the phone, didn't say much, then hung up and began crying. She pressed her back to the wall and slid down to the floor. I ran to her and hugged her.

"What happened, ma?" I asked.

"It's Marlena," she said. "She's dead."

"What do you mean, dead?"

"Her sister was watching her," she said. "She left her in the bathtub without supervision and she drowned. She is dead, son, dead."

I imagined Marlena in the tub wearing clothes and glasses and a red bow. She was smiling. She began sliding into the water. First, her chest, then her neck, then her mouth, then her nose, then her glasses, and then her black hair and red bow until she was lying flat on her back perfectly still in the water, still smiling. Her spirit was ready to move on to another body, I thought, and I cried when I realized what it meant. I would never see her again, we would never laugh together again, and nobody would ever look at me so deeply.

Mother, James, and I went to the funeral. It was my first. My mother didn't stop crying for weeks until she finally quit her job. She gained weight and stopped laughing for a while. She wasn't happy at home, so she took long walks on the beach. Nobody spoke about Marlena again. I covered the walls of the elementary school with bad words and then blamed a kid I could not point out in yearbooks. The principal asked if somebody had flown to Nome, covered the walls in cuss words, and left and I could not say. I denied responsibility yet still had to scrub the walls. James started seeing spirits and telling everybody about it. Some of the teachers, parents, and students said that it was for attention, others believed him. Mother told him to keep it to himself, so he did—for a little while; until his abilities returned and he was able to see things that nobody else could, things that would change the course of our lives forever.

Because of my bad eardrums, I mumbled incoherently for the first seven or eight years and people thought I was dumb, so I kept quiet. When I did talk, my Rs came out like Ws, which made it difficult for a kid named Robert Stark. Anytime I spoke I followed it with, "Sorry for talking so much." School kids can be cruel, and it didn't help to be in a K-12 school.

Older bullies asked my name and then laughed when I answered. I wanted to punch them in the face but they were much bigger, and I didn't want to be beaten any more than I was by my brother, James, and step-father, Dan.

After a long day of harsh teasing, I could not take the humiliation any longer. I sprinted home to find my mother braiding her long hair in a mirror in her bedroom and I watched her strong hands as she stared at me in the reflection.

"What's the matter, son?"

"Nothing," I said, obviously lying.

"You wear your emotions on your sleeve," she said. "It's a good thing. Now tell me the truth, what's the matter?"

"I need a new name," I said. "I get teased every day because I can't say my name right."

"Hmm… What can we do?" Her hands moved in smooth rhythm and seemed like hours passed as I stared at the side of her face waiting for an answer.

"Thousands of people have your same name, Robert, and you know what they do?"   "What?"

"They go by Bob," she said. "It's easy to remember and short to say."

"I don't understand," I said. "Bob is not the same as Robert."

"They are not the same," she said, "but they are." I stared in disbelief. "Bob is short for Robert just like Tom is short for Thomas, or Liz is short for Elizabeth. John is short for Jonathan, Brad is short for Bradley, and…" she paused and smiled. "Dick is short for Richard."

I laughed. "Dick is short for Richard?" I said. "I bet they get teased all the time."

"That's why I didn't name you Richard," she said, removing a hair tie from her wrist to secure the braid. "Come here, dear," she patted the bed. I jumped up and she hugged me. The smell of rose oil smothered all my worries. "Don't let what other people say about you bother you so much. People will be mean and judgmental your entire life, you have to learn how to tune them out."

"Bob..." I whispered. "Bob!" I yelled. "Would I still be the same person?"

"Of course, dear," she said laughing.

I erupted from her arms and stared at myself in the mirror.

"I'm no longer Robert," I said. "I'm Bob… I'm Bob!"

Her eyes twinkled and she smiled. I imagined the bullies' surprised faces the next time they asked my name and I reached around her neck for a quick hug before running outside to count beetles at the pond.

The following day at school, I held my head high in anticipation of a confrontation. When recess came and everybody was on the playground, I was ready. Three of the bullies cornered me near the swing set and formed a circle to prevent my escape.

"Tell us your name, kid!" said the leader, who had a scar above his right eye from a drunk father. I shook my head. "Tell us your name, punk. Or else!"

I inhaled and puffed up my chest. "Bob," I said. "Bob!"

"What do you mean, Bob?" They looked at each other confused. "That's not your name. Tell us your real name."

Scarbrow stepped towards me and I stood my ground, tiny fists clutched at my sides. A crowd grew. I searched for my brother but did not see him.

"Tell us your real name," he said, pushing me.

"Tell us your name or I'll smash your face so bad you won't be able to see for weeks," said another, whose father froze to death the previous winter after huffing gasoline.

"My name is Bob," I said. "Bob!"

Whispers erupted from the crowd of kids. I turned away from them to walk away and Scarbrow punched me under the ribs knocking the wind out of me. I stumbled back and was shoved to the gravel. One kid kicked me in the ribs and ran. I held my arms over my head trying to catch my breath until the duty blew the whistle. I was picked up by the crowd, and for the first time in my life, I noticed a look of admiration in their eyes.

When I was seven years old, I was playing out in the field with two neighborhood girls after returning from Anchorage for hernia surgery. My groin was tender, so I was doing more philosophizing than playing. A row of stitches on my lower abdomen was proof of the operation. The girls were building a snowman when James came outside barking orders. He told them that my testicle had grown to the size of a softball and then tried to make me show them my stitches. They did not laugh and did not want to see it, but he continued to demand that I pull down my pants and show them. I told him to shut up and refused.

"Show them your stitches," he said, "or else."

"I don't want to," I said. "Please."

"Do it," he said, pounding his knuckles together, "or else."

"Or else, what?" I covered my privates with both hands.

"You know what." He punched his left hand with his right.

I shook my head in refusal and he lifted the base of the snowman over his head and threw it at me, bursting open the stitches until blood ran down my legs and I ran inside crying. The girls ran home terrified. James laughed.

Mother, James, and I walked the long sandy beach nearly every day in Nome during the long summer days searching for treasures. We often found poached walruses with tusks removed covered in flies, they smelled awful. Mother was overweight and had long stopped smiling. She was thirteen years younger than Dan and had once been beautiful with child-like excitement, but that was all in the past. Dan was transferred to Anchorage and we were moving, too, so we packed the house in boxes and prepared to leave.

"Every time my daddy was sent to a new duty station," she said, "our family moved. It's the life of a military brat."

"So you always had to say goodbye to your friends?" I asked.

"But we were constantly making new friends," she said. "And seeing new places. That's why I was born in Germany, not America."

"Where is Germany?" I said.

"In Europe."

"Where's Europe?"

"On the other side of the ocean, honey." I examined a starfish and wondered if they existed in Europe. James pointed at a whale blowing mist in the air. Mother continued, "People speak different languages and eat different foods and do different things yet still have the same thing in common."

"What's that?" I asked.

"The desire to be happy," she said.

"I want to go to Germany," I said. "I want to be happy."

"You will son," she said. "I know you will."

Mother found a hundred-dollar bill under a piece of driftwood that she used to bring the three of us to Twin Dragon Chinese Restaurant to share a Poo-Poo Platter to lighten the mood.

W e did overwatch on the valley for two or three days as thousands of soldiers and vehicles arrived by plane. Until the runway was ruined and could not handle anymore. Sully arrived with dozens of cans of Copenhagen and quickly became everybody's best friend. The weather was similar to back home, although I couldn't go inside and warm up. From rain to hail to snow to clear skies all within an hour. We shivered in our thin, summer sleeping bags and bivy sacks, trying not to hyperventilate. If only we would have packed cold-weather gear, I thought. We spooned to try and stay warm and were barely able to fall asleep. Being on guard was a relief from the cold because we were able to walk.

We relocated to a fort in the mountains that looked like it had been around since the time of Christ. We cleaned equipment, ate candy, drank chai, and were served warm bread and hot tea by Kurdish soldiers. We slept on a dirt floor and for the first time, I was grateful for four walls and a roof. One night, our platoon sergeant insisted on having a bonfire so we circled together under the stars to write letters home on scraps of cardboard from MRE boxes. We stayed in the fort a few nights before convoying south, shivering under a piece of parachute Brammer cut as a souvenir. We passed through towns recently cleared by *Peshmerga* with piles of bodies lining the roadside being stacked in trucks like cordwood. At least, I think that is what I saw.

We stopped in an open field outside Irbil to sleep in our trucks or on the ground waiting for the word. Issued a single MRE and bottle of water per day, we rationed everything, including thoughts, words, and tobacco. One soldier even rationed his bowel movements, he hadn't shit since we arrived in-country and was starting to feel sick. We dipped and smoked all day, recycling our chew in plastic bags or empty cans for later. Fireworks lit up the city at night by airplanes we could not see but always heard. I don't remember if the city was Irbil or Mosul, but I remember the lights and the trembling of the earth. I was anxious to enter the city, and quickly learned to avoid using my imagination. But I couldn't help picture people sprinting through blown out streets, children screaming and crying, injured loved ones dragged behind cover while fathers tried to protect their families, shrapnel flying, people dying because they lived in the wrong place; families awakened by planes shivered in dark corners clutching each other, praying, their prayers cut short. I reminded myself that if I felt guilty for every person negatively affected by my presence, I would either be like Loveall, or I would cry. And what use is a crying infantryman? I could be kind, but not sentimental. I remembered the universal spirit existing in ptarmigan, caribou, and human beings. Sometimes my imagination stretched to such extremes that the flashes of light and rumbling of earth represented peace, freedom, and joy to the Iraqi people. I imagined locals smiling with outstretched hands towards the sky, hand drums created the rumbling as they celebrated our arrival. Fireworks are celebratory, I told myself, aren't they?

It had been weeks since we arrived and we still hadn't seen any combat. I was without purpose; my training was not used, I left home to sit around as Marines and the 3rd Infantry Division fought down south. Nobody had spoken to their families or friends and our spirits were low.

Until our company was given a mission one night that was passed down to our lieutenant who passed it down to our platoon sergeant who passed it down to our squad leader who passed it down to us. We circled as a platoon for the platoon sergeant to repeat the mission.

"Tonight is a mission of great importance," he said, and I noticed the redundancy. "One of the last divisions of Republican Guard is north of here, and we're hitting them tonight." Brammer put a hand on my shoulder and smiled, Sully did the same. Everybody nodded and raised their fists. "A few dozen of them with armored vehicles won't give up, so we'll make 'em."

Whispers erupted.

"Fuck yeah," I said.

"At ease," he said. "Remember—we are better trained, tougher, and a whole hell of a lot meaner than them sons of bitches. We came to bring freedom to the Iraqi people. Tonight—we get the chance to do our part."

I did not believe it, and neither did Sully or Brammer. Our platoon sergeant described a bunker and a hill with suspected mortar men emplaced on the hill. The first platoon would clear the bunker as second and third platoons pulled security for our mortar men to engage and destroy the enemy. We raised our weapons in celebration, I held up my grenade launcher. Our lieutenant reminded us that the Republican Guard was Iraq's best-trained soldiers and not to be complacent.

"They aim to destroy our nation and our way of life," our platoon sergeant continued. "Everything our ancestors sweated and bled for. Saddam has tortured, enslaved, and abused these people for too long. We have to stop the genocide. The future of America, Iraq, and humanity is in our hands. Tonight, we make history."

It was what I had signed up to do, to kill the bad guy and help the persecuted.

"It's about time," said Brammer.

"Amen," I said. "I'm tired of sitting around."

Sully shook his head in disbelief. "It ain't happening," he said.

"At ease," said the platoon sergeant. "An interpreter will be in the lead vehicle, your vehicle, Sergeant P."

"Roger sergeant," Sergeant P grinned.

"When we hit the intersection, go two hundred meters

ahead of the convoy to lay down concertina wire across the road to prevent them bastards from escaping. Your gunner needs to be ready to shoot."

"Roger sergeant." Corporal Foran grinned from behind the fifty calibers. "I been ready to kill *hajji* my whole life," he said with a thick southern accent.

"Gunners," yelled the platoon sergeant, with his squeaky voice that was the furthest thing from tough and intimidating. "You'll be using your guns, tonight. So be ready!"

"Roger sergeant," they echoed. Sully and the rest of the gunners made eye contact with each other and nodded.

Our platoon sergeant looked at the lieutenant for words but the humble leader shook his head and nodded.

"Squad leaders," he continued, "check your team leaders; team leaders, check your soldiers. Make sure weapons are clean and night vision has fresh batteries; don't forget to zero your lasers." And then, to my amazement, he laughed. "This is it boys, what we train for. Don't get complacent and don't get scared. Hey—Golden Child," the entire platoon turned to look at me, "you the youngest. You ready?"

"Born ready, sergeant," I said.

"I know you was," he said. "That's why you the Golden Child. Let's move out!"

We moved back to our trucks to field strip rifles, replace batteries, rearrange boxes of MREs and cases of bottled water, and wait. The unbearable waiting I never got used to. I peed out of nervousness half a dozen times; smoked, dipped, and tried to sleep.

"What do you guys think," said Brammer, "are we doing this?"

"No fucking way," said Sully. "We're going to sit around the entire deployment with our thumbs up our asses while Marines do all the fighting." We nodded in agreement. "There is nothing more shameful than to train as infantrymen, come to war, and do nothing but sit around. I'll bet three cans of Copenhagen we don't make contact the entire deployment."

"I'll take that bet," said Brammer, holding out his hand to shake.

Brammer didn't have any fresh chew but Sully ignored the fact. Maybe he wanted to lose because he was tired of giving us dip. Debaser stepped out of the warm cab for the first time in hours to join us.

"All you do is complain, Private Sullivan," he said. "I can hear you bitching inside." His uniform was dry and clean while we were wet and dirty. He was well-rested from not having guard shifts while we were exhausted.

"Come on now sarge," said Sully, "I don't complain, I just tell it how it is."

"Can you go more than an hour without complaining?" said Debaser.

Sullivan thought for a few seconds. "When I finally get out of this shit box organization, I will never complain again, but until then…"

"You'll subject us to your negativity," said Debaser.

"I will keep our morale high by laughing," said Sullivan.

And laugh we did, everybody besides Debaser, who

finished his cigarette, started the truck to turn on the heater, and sat in the driver's seat.

"I'm tired of spooning you fuckers while the war is fought down south," said Sully. "I'm getting less action here than I did at home."

"We all know you didn't get any action back home," said Brammer. "And we all know that you love spooning the Golden Child."

"Don't fucking call me that," I said. They all laughed.

"You guys can fuck right off," said Sully.

"Don't worry, Sully," said Brammer, "you'll owe me three cans by morning."

As the sun sank below the horizon my nerves almost got the best of me. The soldier who couldn't shit tried multiple times without luck. I peed at least a dozen times per hour. We donned night vision goggles and began guard. Everybody knows the enemy hits at sunrise and sunset.

A cold breeze swept in as our company commander called for platoon leaders and Lieutenant Spencer briskly walked over. I started to believe that it was real and started shaking again. LT returned and called over the platoon sergeant who yelled for squad leaders. Hollywood grabbed his rifle and green notebook and then jogged in their direction.

"What do you guys think," said Brammer, packing a chew, "we doing this?"

"How many times do I need to say it?" said Sully. "The most action we'll get is from dirty magazines." Even Alvarez laughed then, and he always kept to himself.

"Ya'll are fucking crazy," said Alvarez. "We got no control over nothing, so go with the flow."

Like our LT, Alvarez rarely spoke, but he had more military experience than the three of us and was well respected.

"They're probably canceling the mission," I said.

"Shut the fuck up back there," said Debaser from the front seat. "You guys complain like schoolgirls. Especially you, Sullivan, you deserve a medal."

"Yeah, I do," said Sully. "For whooping your bitch ass," he whispered.

"What was that?" Said Debaser, stepping out of the Humvee. "What did you say, Private Sullivan?"

"'I deserve a medal for being a wise-ass,'" he said.

"That's what I thought you said, private."

Debaser paced around the hood of the Humvee without another word. Brammer removed his chew, put it in an old can, and asked Sully for one.

"You just took one out," said Sully. "And you'll empty my can in a pinch."

Brammer snickered, "That's bullshit and you know it."

"Get the fuck outta here," replied Sullivan, with an accent like Alvarez, who was from Yonkers, New York.

"My cans are in the bottom of my ruck," said Brammer. "And besides, you'll owe me three by the end of the night."

"I only have two dips left in this can," said Sully, "and if I give you one, I will have none."

"You need to open a fresh can anyway," I said, "for the mission tonight."

"You mother fuckers."

Sully reached over the side of the truck to dig in his ruck, which was hanging by shoulder straps on the wooden side rails.

"You guys are gonna lose your fucking teeth," said Alvarez, the only tobacco-free man in the platoon, probably in the army. "Who are you gonna sleep with then?"

"That's the least of my worries," said Sully, looking at Debaser while rubbing his fists.

Hollywood jogged back to the truck smiling like a movie star. It was so dark and he was so black all I could see were his teeth and eyes.

"Golden Child," he said, and everybody snickered. "You're moving to the lead vehicle to pull security for the terp."

"What do you mean?" I said. "This is my truck, my squad."

"Not tonight," he said. "Platoon sergeant asked for you specifically."

I shook my head in embarrassment as the guys laughed.

"But what if we make contact," I said. "I want to be with my squad."

"Too bad," he said. "Grab your shit, head out."

"Roger sergeant."

I unhooked my ruck and walked across the field wondering how I had gotten into the situation. I would be laying down the wire in front of everybody else as Foran fired over my head. I reached their truck, hung my ruck, and sized up the crew. I hated Sergeant P and Foran, they were both power-hungry assholes, and Foran was an open racist. He had a bald head like a chicken egg, stained teeth, and beady eyes; he resembled a rat, not a wise one like Splinter but one that spreads disease. Enlisted over eight years and still a corporal, he was demoted twice for beating up women. The driver was a soft-spoken Jewish guy from New York named Roche, who refused to drink alcohol but chugged cough syrup instead. He locked himself in his barracks room on weekends to binge masturbate while the rest of us went out to mingle. He was weird, but I liked him. Sergeant P had a Ranger tab that meant nothing because all he seemed to learn at Ranger School was how to chain smoke cigarettes and treat people like shit. He was built like a high school cross country runner, with the eyes of someone whose hardest moment was burying a pet hamster. Private Brian was nineteen and from Cleveland; his skills consisted of freestyle rapping, crip walking, and singing R&B. Kershner was tall and goofy and looked like Big Bird on Sesame Street, I never heard him talk. They were not the soldiers I wanted to fight with, not like the guys in my squad.

The cloudy sky opened to reveal patches of stars as jets flew over and explosions were seen and felt. The company lined up our trucks, and the interpreter was nowhere to be found.

"'We are sons of thunder,'" I whispered to myself, quoting the only scripture I knew.

The entire company of soldiers, well over a hundred and forty, began to yell from the backs of our trucks. And the interpreter climbed in out of breath. He sat at the front of the left bench beside Foran, who stood behind the fifty-caliber machine gun. He was forty-three years old with a full beard while I was a baby-faced teenager with enough stubble to be excited. He spoke perfect English and claimed to be from Florida, but I didn't believe him. The only Muslims I knew were in prison or on television, and they always represented violence. His translator position was advertised in a Miami newspaper, he said, so he left his family and their home security business for the financial opportunity of a lifetime. One year in Iraq would earn him close to three-hundred thousand dollars and pay off all of his debts. I would make around twenty-five thousand. Our conversation ended. He held out his hand to shake Foran's who stared ahead without budging.

Our truck was leading the convoy, and as we began moving, Private Brian and I started singing Sublime's "What I Got" to ease the tension. The interpreter stared ahead and Foran shook his head as we drove toward fireworks for what seemed like hours. Then we sang Blind Melon, 4 Non Blondes, and Alan Jackson. Anything we both knew to relieve the fear. We passed shanties on the sides of the road and small dwellings where people ran at us as we approached and I pointed my rifle at them just in case.

"Ten minutes until we're on the objective," yelled Sergeant P from the passenger seat. "Keep your eyes peeled and shut the fuck up."

My mind raced, my eyes scanned, and every sensation intensified. All I could see were green fields and rolling hills. I recalled the day before I left for basic training when my friend in Seward, Bruce Rockefeller, promised to enlist if I was ever shot at. Will I tell him if something happens tonight? I wondered. I imagined my brother pacing in solitary, my mother in a red dress and red lipstick talking on the phone before visiting, Elliot putting on fresh rain and patchouli oil after a hot shower. I wondered how long it would take for her to forget me if she hadn't already? Maybe she would plant a tree by the skatepark if I died. Hell, I was only 18, I couldn't die. I needed to meet my father first.

We turned left on a dirt road and Roche turned off the headlights and went in blackout drive, accelerating towards the hillside once all vehicles turned behind us. I thought I was going to piss my pants, I scanned the roadsides.

"Get ready to set the wire," yelled Sergeant P.

Tracers came from the hillside followed by a volley of explosions I had never heard before.

"Mortars!" shouted Sergeant P. "Get down!"

I ducked, covered my head, and hoped. A mortar exploded hundreds of meters behind us, as orange and green tracers flew in every direction. The hill was coming up fast. Our gunners unleashed and the interpreter prayed. Foran began firing the fifty so loud my ears rang and Roche punched it forward as bullets snapped overhead. Our company pulled off behind as we pushed forward. I held my breath and held on to the wooden railings to keep from flying over the tailgate. The interpreter curled up at Foran's feet with interlaced fingers behind his neck, still praying.

"You fuckin' coward," said Foran, smacking his helmet. "Get up and shut up!"

A blast of wind ripped back my helmet and I held it with my non-firing hand. I could see structures, vehicles, and tiny people running around on the hill.

"Shut the fuck up!" yelled Foran, and he kicked the interpreter.

We came to a screeching halt in the truck and Sergeant P yelled, "Go, go, go!"

And Brian and I leaped over the tailgate and ran to the hood to untangle two strands of wire as tracers continued flying overhead followed by loud explosions that got closer to our rear. We cut the wire that held them to the hood, yanked them to the ground, found the handles, separated them, grabbed a strand, and sprinted ten meters ahead to stretch it across the road. It took forever. As we hunched forward and ran back for the second strand, a pair of headlights appeared fifty meters ahead. The vehicle stopped and began a three-point turn.

"Light it up?" yelled Foran, followed by a pause that seemed to last forever but was probably only a couple of seconds.

"Only if they fire," said Sergeant P.

I pointed my grenade launcher at the vehicle while crouching beside the Humvee. I took a deep breath as it traveled back in the direction it came. Brian and I stretched out the second strand of wire and then returned to the side of the truck to pull security. I was out of breath while trying to keep my night vision goggles from fogging up. The sound of mortars, bombs, gunfire, and shouting echoed in the valley. After our mortar platoon was set and calibrated, they launched a volley of rounds that fell short of the target.

"Kill those motherfuckers," I shouted at the top of my lungs, watching and sweating.

The earth shook behind us as their mortar men got closer and closer to us and tracers flew in every direction and the god damn interpreter continued to pray.

"Shut the fuck up," yelled Foran, after firing a volley with the fifty cal. "I'll kill your *hajji* ass if you don't shut the fuck up!"

The interpreter shut up.

The fifty cal and mark 19 gunners continued to fire while the rest of us watched for ground troops. A mortar exploded close enough to spray rubble in my face.

"That was a close one," said Sergeant P, and we all laughed hysterically.

After what seemed like hours but was probably only minutes, one of our mortar rounds hit a building and exploded like in the movies and we all cheered.

"Kill those mother fuckers!" That was all I could seem to think and say.

Our mortar men destroyed everything on the hill within minutes until nothing but flames and smoke were left. A cease-fire was echoed followed by a cloak of silence so thick I didn't know if I was alive or dead. But I had never felt so alive.

"Load up," came over the radio.

"Load it up," said Sergeant P.

"Load up!" was echoed by every soldier.

I climbed over the tailgate and sat on the wooden bench watching soldiers sprint to their trucks, wondering if anybody was hit. Roche turned the truck around and we sped past everybody to take the lead. The interpreter huddled in the corner crying until Foran threatened his life again and he sat on the bench trembling. Brian and I hung our outside legs over the tailgate and stared past each other with our rifles at the ready. I had never been so grateful to be alive.

When the entire convoy returned to the highway and word went out that we didn't have any injuries, victory cheers erupted. We moved south without words as jets passed overhead and bombs continued to drop in the distance. I returned to my truck just in time for a cursing Sullivan to hand over three cans to a laughing Brammer. We stayed awake for hours dipping and talking. The guy who hadn't shit, shit his pants during the firefight, it was fucking hilarious.

I t was the day before third grade when we moved to Eagle River. Mother and Dan rarely spoke. We lived in a one-story house with a backyard that shared a fence with the elementary school. The house had a crawl space and an attic, a fireplace that didn't produce heat, and fake brick as siding. It looked like houses in Missouri. James was too old and cool to hang out with his little brother. He had gotten into girls, upright bass, marijuana, skateboarding, and Metallica. The only thing we did together was go skateboarding, and dye our hair crazy colors, not for more than a couple of years though until he drifted away completely.

Mother became friends with a group of traveling psychics who were teaching classes on reading tarot cards, crystal balls, palms, and auras. I didn't understand why she was so adamant about involving her sons, but she insisted that we tap into our hidden powers. After a few months of training, James, our mother, and I attended psychic fairs in hotel lobbies in

Anchorage where I was a door greeter, my mother read tarot cards and James did crystal ball readings. People lined up at my brother's table, partly because he was the youngest person doing readings, at eleven or twelve, partly because he had a reputation for being accurate.

During his final reading, he told a lady that her son would die in a car accident the following week, and she stormed out of the hotel in a frenzy. Everybody was startled, especially James, and a week later, a crying woman called the house asking for him. Her son was dead, and she insisted on knowing his secret.

James never did another reading or mentioned seeing another spirit, instead, he started running away for weeks on end to use heroin and other drugs. I missed my big brother so bad it made me furious; I channeled my anger into baseball and skateboarding, becoming obsessively good at both.

Mother built a pitching mound in the backyard and used a cheap mask and mitt to catch my wild pitches. She always wore jean shorts, no matter what the weather. She tapped her left thigh to aim left, right thigh to aim right, raised a finger for a high fastball, and made a downward motion for a low ball. It didn't matter when my low was too low, high too high, and left or right directly over the plate, she gave positive encouragement no matter what. It was our favorite activity together, a bond built on baseball. We didn't talk about James or Dan or my real father or any of the problems we faced as a family, we never did, we focused on what was right in front of us, baseball.

Since I was a wild pitcher, especially when my emotions got the best of me, the ball bounced off the plate or dirt and struck her shins and knees so hard that she was consistently covered in bruises yet never made a sound. She often removed the mitt, shook her hand, and said, "Good pitch," or "You're throwing hard, Robert." And every year I tried out for the All-Star team—I made it, and she was always Team Mom.

She attended every game despite the weather, drove players to games and practices whose parents were unable, and signed me up for every camp that came to town. Everybody loved and respected her, everybody besides Dan and James.

A new coach from out of town showed great interest in my pitching ability and offered to coach me privately. I was ten or eleven at the time. I thought it was odd that he always wanted to go to the gym after practice to use the sauna or shower, and it was especially odd that he would look at me with strange eyes and an erection. I was afraid of him, terrified actually, too afraid to tell anybody. He told my mother that he was having a sleepover with a group of kids and when I was dropped off at his house he told my mother that nobody was able to come but that it would still be okay if I stayed. He had already ordered pizza and picked out the Lazer Disc Movies we would watch. She trusted him, after months of building rapport, and said okay. I was too afraid to say anything to her for fear that she would be disappointed that I didn't want to practice with him anymore. My pitching skills had really increased, and she constantly talked about me going to college on a baseball scholarship and maybe playing in the big leagues one day. I didn't want to let her down.

After eating pizza and root beer floats and watching a

movie I forgot, we went to sleep, him in his room and me on the living room floor. I awoke to him standing over me naked suggesting I come to his bedroom. I refused, and he persisted. I stood and walked with heavy legs toward candlelight shining down the hallway from the back left door. As he walked in, I stood shaking by his bed and he told me everything would be okay and not to worry. He climbed in bed and pulled back the sheets on the other side, suggesting I get in. I walked around the bed and smelled something so disgusting I had no idea what it was. I got in the cold sheets and shook in fear, thinking of a plan to escape. He rolled to his side and put his disgusting, hairy hand on my tiny chest and I jumped out of bed, ran down the hall, sprinted down the stairs, and burst out the locked door into a cold, night. Where I ran and ran and ran in my tiny white underwear hiding in bushes every time I saw headlights. Until I made it home an hour later to my mother's surprise. When I told her what happened, she called the police, and I didn't see him again. Mother and I never played catch again, and that was the end of my baseball career.

We moved to a subdivision where mother put up a badminton net and built a couple of skateboard ramps to use in the cul-de-sac. Every day, she opened the front door and said, "Go outside and play, Robert," and I would skate alone for hours.

She was on a first-name basis with the cops who consistently searched for James and brought him home. He would shake and sweat and eat and sleep for days before running away again. It was exhausting for our family. We never knew what he would say or do and he beat me up regularly and justified it by "making me tough" for times he wouldn't be around. When he was fifteen and I was twelve, he made me swear not to tell anybody what he was about to tell me.

"I robbed a liquor store last night," he said. "The cops are hunting for me. I'm going to hide here a few days before skipping town."

I didn't believe him, I never did anymore. I nodded and acted like he didn't say anything, until the following day in Language Arts class when my name was called over the intercom and all my classmates oooh'd and ahhh'd. In the office, two cops stood behind my crying mother.

"Your brother needs help," they said. "And you have a chance to help him."

"Please, Robert," said mother, crying. "If you know anything, tell them. James needs your help."

They pushed *Record* on the tape player and I was recorded trying to help my brother by telling them everything he told me. The tape was used at his trial, and for two bottles of tequila and three hundred dollars, my big brother was sentenced to seven years in a maximum-security prison where he did not rehabilitate.

Mother and I visited him at McLaughlin Youth Facility in Anchorage, but it was cut short when he began yelling at our mother. She cried on the way back to the mini-van, I cried with her. We visited him a few months later at Cook Inlet Pretrial, where he was obviously changing. He told me a story through a thick barrier of glass with a phone to our ears.

"I was on my bunk chillin', mindin' my business," he said, with an accent I had only heard on rap albums and gangster movies. "When this little bitch came stormin' into my cell, runnin' his trap. He called me a punk, and you don't call nobody a fuckin' punk in here, Bobby. He said that he was gonna show me what prison life was all about. I laughed, Ha Ha Ha, and did my best to pay the mothafucka no mind, I just kept layin' on my back with my hands behind my head, eyes closed, tryin' to block him out like a little fly buzzin' in my ear. But, let me tell you, little brother, nobody can stand buzzin' too long, and the last thing I want is people to think I'm a bitch or somethin'. So I got down from my bunk and stood up, like this," he set the phone down and held up his arms. "You see, Little Bobby, that's the way it is 'round here, you don't have to fight if you don't want to, but then you'll be somebody's bitch, and Little Devil ain't nobody's bitch! So I stood up, like this, and threw my hands in the air and "Wham!" that motherfucka starts stabbin'

70

me with a shim until my celly came in and yanked him off. He got me six times though, so I'll have some mean ass scars to show." He laughed hysterically as I stared in disbelief. Whom had my big brother become?

Mother felt indebted to his cellmate, so she visited him, put money on his books, and accepted his phone calls. It did not seem to bother Dan, he probably didn't know. He was too busy golfing with fellow Masons and keeping up on TV shows to notice.

My brother's cell mate's mother fell down a flight of stairs and died. He was given two weeks with an ankle monitor to attend the services and handle affairs. Mother and I went from Eagle River to Anchorage every day to taxi him around town. She gave him twenty dollar bills and let him kiss her neck and whisper in her ear as she giggled before asking her to hang around a few hours because he would need a ride somewhere else. I didn't understand why she continued to bring me along, but I didn't say anything—I felt the need to protect her in whatever way I could. The two of us spent a lot of quality time at the Northway Mall drinking Orange Julius and eating Mrs. Cinnabon. After the funeral, he somehow removed his ankle monitor and went on the run. He would hide behind the seats in the mini-van when we passed a police car. Mother got a rush breaking the rules, especially after being an underappreciated housewife for eight years. He introduced her to a black family in the Mountain View Neighborhood who dabbled in illegal forms of employment. She began to visit them regularly.

Victor Stern was doing life in Spring Creek Correctional Facility, he was less than forty years old and had not had a visitor in over fifteen years. Mother agreed to bring his son to Seward once they were on the visiting list, and when the time came, his son was nowhere to be found. But mother kept her word, like she always did, and drove a hundred and forty miles in a blizzard to visit a man in prison for murder. The first time they locked eyes, she knew they would marry. She believed they had been married in past lives. She began spending weekends in Seward, avoiding Dan completely when she returned to Eagle River and sleeping downstairs in James' old room. After about a month, she sat me down one night to talk.

"You are a very smart young man," she said. "You know that."

I shook my head and stared at the floor. I was an athlete, not an intellectual. Maybe I was smart in early elementary school, before mathematics and standardized tests shattered my self-confidence, but I had long since stopped trying and succumbed to the role of dumb athlete.

"I know that you know what is happening between Dan and me," she said. "But I have lived with neglect too many years." Her eyes welled up. "I have been playing housewife for a man who would rather watch television and go to meetings than spend time with me." She dabbed the corner of her eyes with a paper towel. "I used to be beautiful, and happy, and I am still young. When a man does not appreciate what his woman does for him," she said, "it is time for the woman to find a man who will. Remember that, son."

"Yes, ma'am."

"I have been waiting eight years for things to change," she said, "but nothing has."

I searched for words of comfort but nothing came. I stared at the floor to keep from crying. I missed my brother; I was ashamed for telling on him and tearing our family apart.

"So what do I do now, son?" she said. "You know the pillowcase upstairs, that says, 'God—grant me the serenity to accept the things I cannot change, courage to change the things I can, and wisdom to know the difference?'" I nodded. "I finally accept that this relationship will never change. So I'm leaving Dan in Eagle River and moving to Seward."

"What?" I said. "Leaving Eagle River? But this is our home, my friends are here." I bit my trembling lip. "I could maybe go to college on a baseball scholarship. Can't we just get an apartment downtown until I finish school? I'm a freshman, it's only a few more years."

She leaned forward, put her face in her hands, and sobbed. I rubbed her back and cried. It was all my fault, I never should have told on my brother.

"I am so sorry to do this to you, Robert," she said, "but I need to get out of here. To get away from him. I am moving next week, I already decided. You can come or you can stay with your friends to finish high school." I sobbed as she rubbed my back. "It's okay to cry, son," she said. "A man without emotion is no man at all."

We cried and hugged until she pulled away to wipe her eyes and stare at the wall.

I moved to a friend's place to finish my freshman year in a concrete basement. I wanted to be with my mother and brother; I wanted to call my real dad, Bert, and live with him, but I had no idea where he was or how to contact him. I started drinking, smoking bud, and using tobacco.

By the time the school year ended and I moved to Seward, my mother had remarried. She was living in an equal housing opportunity apartment that everybody in town called "Crackside," because only poor kids and drug addicts lived there. We could see snow-covered mountains, water, and beach from our living room window. Mother was either on the phone, at the prison, or working as a hotel receptionist. I started stealing from her wallet to buy cheap vodka, skipping school multiple times a week, and staying in the shadows. My brother had been transferred to the same prison as my mother's husband, and every time I visited him, he had another tattoo and another violent story. He hated our mother and her husband and refused to visit with them. Eventually, I felt too ashamed of "being a snitch" that I stopped visiting altogether. I had only hurt him worse, and I was hurting bad enough inside that I didn't want anybody to see.

After moving to Seward my sophomore year, I became friends with a senior named Bruce Rockefeller. He was good at skating, despite being six foot four two hundred plus pounds, he drank a lot of beer and always had the best weed. He drove a blue Volvo station wagon and never had problems buying alcohol. He always had a twelve-pack of Icehouse and a pocket rocket of liquor. He was the perfect friend for somebody like me.

"One is to get us drunk, the other is to keep us warm," he would say.

We often skipped school and turned a typical two-hour hike into an all-day drunken adventure. We rarely had the proper gear and always took turns breaking brush or post-holing in snow. We climbed huge Sitka spruce trees to drink and smoke in the branches or built fires on the beach to do the same. I thought of Bruce as a brother, he always had my back.

Spontaneous day trips were an escape from the consistent cloud cover in Seward. We drove the two-lane Seward

Highway north to Moose Pass to drink at Trail Lake, or hike to Carter and Crescent Lakes to drink in the mountains as others fished. Our favorite game was opening a beer, taking a drink then passing it back and forth until it was finished. We could drink an entire twelve-pack in less than thirty minutes. We never talked about the future, politics, school, or anything that was going on in our own families. We were focused on having fun at the moment.

Summer in Alaska is the peak season for road construction. I had recently bought a video camera with tip money from bussing tables and Bruce thought it would be funny to run over construction cones on camera. I agreed, and luckily it was Sunday and nobody was working. When I had the camera steady, Bruce swerved within a few inches of the cones.

"You ready?" he said.

"Almost," I said, then hit record. "Ready."

He accelerated from thirty-five to sixty-five despite double traffic fines or the fact that we were drunk and stoned. Jerking the wheel to the right, we struck the first cone with a loud thump and laughed as it bounced over the windshield and rolled in the ditch. He held a direct course as we blasted dozens of cones and laughed, laughed, laughed.

Another time—we had returned from a drunk hike and were cruising the strip smoking weed while playing our favorite drinking game when Bruce said that he was heading to a friend's cabin for a party. I didn't like his friend, so I asked him to drop me off in the harbor so I could kick hack instead. He acted deaf and drove straight through the harbor.

"Come on, man," I said. "Drop me off at Eagle, I won't go to his house."

But he kept driving, passed canneries on the right and a cemetery on the left, over three bridges until turning right on Nash Road, the same road that leads to the prison. What could I do? If I opened the door and jumped I would probably get hurt and not be able to work. If I grabbed the steering wheel and jerked the car into the ditch we would both get hurt. I had no options.

"Let me the fuck out," I said.

He laughed and kept driving, turning up the volume and singing Blind Melon's "No Rain."

When we arrived at the cabin, seven senior football players were wasted and the smell inside reminded me of my former baseball coach's bedroom and almost made me puke. The guy I didn't like grabbed my shoulder and spat the words within a few inches from my face, "The slut will be here any minute."

"What are you talking about?" I said.

"You're here to join us, right?" He furrowed his brow and licked his lips.

"Join you for what?"

"To gang bang some dumb bitch."

I paused, looked around, and noticed the testosterone.

"No," I said, "I'm not here to join you."

I walked outside as Bruce yelled my name from behind and a woman in her thirties closed the door on a beat-up car. We locked eyes without words and I started running as hard as I could to the sound of cheering and howling behind me. I sprinted past headstones from an old graveyard and kept on running.

Another time—It was a dark, windy winter night in the year 2000. We survived Y2K, so there was reason to party. Bruce and I were at a friend's house where we often went to smoke and drink during school hours because his parent's let us. The dad was a former logger with a blonde mullet and icy eyes. He had a low, hoarse voice and a slight whistle due to a missing front tooth. He delivered mail part-time and told stories of growing up in Oregon as a logger full-time. He and his wife watched fishing and hunting shows all day together while smoking cigarettes and buds. He would get so drunk he could only open his left eye while he mumbled cuss words as he drank. We were relieved when he reached that point because beforehand, he would pick fights with us teenagers and occasionally spit on his wife and call her a whore or a bitch or some other awful name. Because he tended to get violent when drinking whiskey, his wife asked us to keep it out of the house.

Bruce and I were taking waterfalls, a hit of weed swallowed down with beer, and when the beer was gone, Bruce jogged to the Volvo and came back with a bottle of Jack tucked under his jacket. The wife pleaded that he leave it outside, but Bruce didn't listen, so we started taking shots.

"And for you, old man?" Bruce held out the bottle to the old logger.

"He doesn't need any of that shit," she said. "He has to work tomorrow."

"I know damn well what'll happen if I drink that shit," he said.

Bruce stood over him on the couch, he was bigger than the old man.

"You can't hang with the young guns anymore, can you, you old bitch?" said Bruce.

The man wheezed and laughed and stubbed out his cigarette in the ashtray as his wife shook her head and stared at the TV. Smoke was everywhere, even when they opened the refrigerator smoke came out.

"I drank more Jack in my life than you'll ever taste, boy," said the logger.

"Jesus Christ," said Bruce, shaking his head. "I knew you were a bitch."

"Quit bringing that shit in my house," said the wife. "And get the hell out of here."

Bruce laughed, took another hit from the pipe, and chased it down with a swill.

"The wife wants me to start taking her easy," said the

man. "And I think I will. So thanks, boys, but no Jack for me, not today."

"That's cool," I said, embarrassed. "It's your house."

Their son sat on the couch staring at the TV without saying a word.

"I came here to drink with you," said Bruce, "and now you're going to bitch out and disrespect me in front of everybody."

The logger shook his head and laughed. "You're a real fucking prick, you know that."

Bruce smiled.

"If my dad doesn't want to drink, he doesn't have to."

"Shut the fuck up," said Bruce, pointing at our friend while standing over him. "This is between me and your old man." He turned toward the father. "Are you going to make me drink alone?"

As the old logger grabbed the bottle, tipped it back, and swilled a quarter bottle, Steve Irwin talked on the TV. His wife shook her head, covered her eyes, and lit another cigarette as the son walked to his bedroom and closed the door.

"Woo boy," said the logger. "Hot damn! That there boys is how you take a drink."

Bruce patted his shoulder and hollered, "That is what the fuck I'm talking about."

We passed the bottle until it was gone. I blacked out. How much time passed—I will never know, but when I came to, I was lying on a bed in a smoky apartment while Bruce yelled, "The ducks that quack their asses out of Alaskan waters are no fucking way the same ducks as those in Oregon!"

And the old logger said, "I have hunted them my entire life, you son of a bitch. What the fuck do you know about ducks, anyway? Have you ever killed an animal before?"

They began to wrestle on the bed and I moved to an empty chair beside a chain-smoking Vietnam Vet seated by an open window. It was freezing in the apartment, and a bottle of Oxycontin was on the table. A skinny native man with long, black hair entered and sat next to the window to smoke. I bummed one and joined them but felt like I would puke. The Vietnam Vet went to the bathroom and I noticed a dragging leg. He was short, fat, and white with balding gray hair; not what I expected in a war veteran. The wrestling match ended and Bruce asked for pills. The veteran handed two to each of us and we swallowed them down. I blacked out again. And when I came to, we were high centered in a ditch in the Volvo on hard-packed snow. Bruce was spinning the tires and revving the engine, trying to gain traction without luck. He slammed it in reverse, and then drive, trying to rock it out, but nothing worked. The engine echoed from nearby houses along with Bruce's yelling.

"Let's get the hell out of here, boys," said the logger from the back seat. He opened the door and ran. It was snowing so hard everything was white; I had no idea what time it was but it sure was bright. Bruce began to punch the steering wheel until the horn broke and started honking incessantly.

"Let's go," I said. "Let's fucking go!"

I opened the passenger side door as he slammed it in reverse and the door got stuck on an ice berm and ripped open, never to close again. With three doors wide open, we followed the logger's footprints to the alley that led to their house. We snuck in the front door and went into the son's room to hide under dirty clothes on the floor.

"What the fuck are you guys doing here?" he said. "You guys need to leave."

"Shh…" said Bruce. "Just let us sleep here."

"You guys are so fucking stupid," he said. "Get the fuck out of here."

A knock came from the front door.

"Don't answer it," I mumbled. "Please… don't answer it."

He turned on a light, put on pajamas, and left. Bruce turned off the light.

"Just act like everybody is sleeping," said Bruce. "Don't tell them we're here."

The knocking became louder until he opened the front door. We could hear voices but not words.

"You guys have to come out," he said, turning on the light. "The cops found your car, Bruce, they followed your footprints in the snow. You fucking dumb shits."

"Dammit," said Bruce.

"You guys are fucking idiots," he said. "Don't say anything about my dad. He'll get fired."

Bruce patted my back as we stood. "We're royally fucked," he said.

We were handcuffed and put in the back of the cop car. Bruce kicked the doors and called the officer names while I stayed quiet. Because I was underage and not driving, the officer brought me to my mother's apartment to be in her custody. Bruce winked and smiled from the back seat as they drove away. He was charged with minor consumption and driving under the influence, I was charged with minor consumption. I did an alcohol rehabilitation class which consisted of watching a movie with Michael Keaton as a struggling alcoholic, lying on paperwork and questionnaires, and not being drunk while in class. It did nothing other than make me feel more shame, which gave me more of a reason to drink.

I was fourteen the first time I saw Elliot. She was seated on the big two-step at the skate park admiring the mountains and waves. Her back was turned away from the guys who were trying to impress her, they called her name and did tricks and she acted like she couldn't hear them. I couldn't help staring at the side of her face and back. Her short hair was bleached and she had freckles. She wore blue slacks and a blue sweatshirt with holes for her thumbs. I landed the best tricks of my life that day, and I don't think she saw one. Winter Formal was a few weeks away, and all the guys were asking out all the girls. I was too shy to ask anybody, and the only person I wanted to go with wouldn't look at me. One of her friends told me that she was waiting for me to ask her, but I didn't believe it. I didn't believe anybody other than Bruce wanted anything to do with me. Until another friend, who had been her friend since Kindergarten, told me the same thing.

"If you don't ask her," he said. "I will. She's hot."

"Go ahead," I said. "I don't care." By the age of 14, I was a master of acting like I didn't care. He asked her out and she said no, then she showed up at my mother's apartment.

"Are you going to ask me to the dance or not?" she said, standing in the doorway.

I shrugged, "Do you really want to go with me?"

She shook her head and smiled. "Don't be an idiot. I've liked you this whole time."

We went to Peking Restaurant in our fancy clothes, it was one of three options in town, and we awkwardly slow danced. It was the beginning of our inseparability. It was before Tinder and online dating, so we moved slowly by American standards. After two months of spending every day together, we had still not kissed.

We went with some friends across the bay to explore an abandoned metal platform once used to load wood chips in barges for shipment to China. The wind howled as white caps sprayed cold water. A sea otter floated and rolled, cracking a mussel with sharp teeth. Termination dust swirled on mountain peaks, and Elliot's pink devil's lock whipped around as we held hands and walked down the beach then up a grated metal ramp. To the east, at the base of a glacier, were the lights from the prison, where my brother lived. To the south were Fox, Hive, and Rugged Islands, which opened up to open water, where my imagination lived. To the west was Seward, a tiny town built on a narrow strip of land at the base of two mountains. And to the north, an endless spruce forest surrounded by green and white mountains with a narrow highway that leads through Canada. I dreamed of the day I could take that road out of town to explore the world and escape my circumstances.

Our friends were jumping up and down on the metal platform while yanking the handrails and trying to shake the tower. They banged their skateboard trucks against the metal. Elliot and I didn't make a sound, we were too shy to talk around people. The platforms became smaller the higher we climbed, and when we were at the second to last level, we watched our two friends take turns climbing the wobbly ladder to sit alone on top. I put my arm over her shoulders and pulled her close to smell her hair. Patchouli, Nag Champa, and Fresh Rain oil mixed with saltwater and the cleanest air in the world. We looked at each other from inches away and smiled. When she looked away, I cursed myself for missing the opportunity.

Our friends warned us of the tiny platform without guard rails, cautioning us to stay low or risk being blown to our deaths. Elliot grabbed the rungs without hesitation and climbed. I tried to be a gentleman, but I could not help looking at her perfect butt in blue slacks. She stopped and looked down with a look that said, I know what you're doing, but I acted like I was looking north toward my future until she continued climbing and I looked back at her butt and legs. I followed her onto the platform that was no larger than four feet by four feet where we sat crossed-legged with knees touching as wind gusts ripped. She put her hands on my knees and I did the same, I had never seen a more beautiful view. The girl I had grown to love, my new best friend, with a background of mountains and waves. After a couple of minutes, we simultaneously leaned forward and kissed like we had been kissing our entire lives. We stopped and smiled, touching each other's faces with our fingertips then rubbed the tips of our noses together in an Eskimo kiss. My shame, and the entire dark world, disappeared.

Mother continued working hard at the hotel picking up shifts for extra loot. She visited Victor regularly and allowed his father to move into my bedroom, forcing me on the couch. He didn't do anything but lay in bed smoking cigarettes, take naps and watch Judge Judy. He ate scrambled eggs and jelly sandwiches with spicy sausage links. I was embarrassed by my home life, it seemed like anytime Bruce or Elliot came over mother was lying in bed with her door cracked whispering on the phone.

"Oh, Mr. Stern," she would say. "Of course, I'll wear the red shirt and jeans you love so much." Silence followed by giggling. "Don't be so ornery. Yeah, we're making dinner right now. What do you want to have for dinner?" She laughed. "Of course, we can eat that when you get home, but we have to make more money than what this hotel job pays to eat like that." Silence. "You're right, Mr. Stern, for now, it's enough."

I began to hate her.

Despite all of it, Elliot started staying the night in a bed on the living room floor.

My partying was out of control and my lack of attendance at school was a direct result. I barely passed my classes and quit playing sports. My identity as an athlete was gone, and since I had long thought myself stupid, my identity was as a drunk and stoner who didn't care about school or rules. Victor tried to ground me for staying out all night and not adhering to my mother's rules, but Bruce teased me so bad about being grounded by somebody in prison that I refused to listen. Eventually, my mother kicked me out in the spring of junior year with snow still on the ground. A few people offered places to stay with their parents, but I refused. I wasn't a charity case. So I borrowed a tent and pitched it in the woods on school grounds where I could wake up early enough to shower in the locker rooms before anybody arrived.

That lasted for a couple of weeks until a family that recently lost a son in a jet skiing accident heard about my situation and offered me a place to stay. I agreed, moved into a small room upstairs, and blacked out the first night puking in their bathtub. When I woke up in the morning, wondering if it was all a dream, I stumbled into their smoky living room as they stared hard at me. He was a Vietnam Veteran turned counselor at the prison, she was the City Mayor. I respected them for their positions, so when they told me that I could not live like that in their home and would have to follow some rules, I listened… for a little while.

Elliot waited almost an entire year before having sex. Once we started, it was all I wanted to do. I had found my new identity, sex was the only way I felt validated. My friendships were stagnant, truancies regular, family relationships non-existent, and athletics ignored. Elliot talked me into taking ceramics class with her and the only thing I made was a pinch pot tea-candle holder to get a D minus. I was intimidated to try at anything in front of her or anybody, so I started studying books on Tantra and Kama Sutra, trying to impress her the only way I knew how.

When she graduated a year ahead of me and left for college in Oregon, I felt abandoned once again. She wanted to stay together, but I could not believe that she would keep her fidelity with a piece of trash like me. So I broke up with her and started snorting pills, drinking more, and eating mushrooms. Victor's father had moved out of my bedroom and my mother wanted me to move back in, and since I had burned the bridge where I lived because I couldn't stop partying, I did.

All of these stories, actions, thoughts, and events led to a single moment… When I saw an escape in a uniformed soldier on top of the common stairs. An escape from my mother's telephone-based love-life, from whispering locals who knew my family history, from being another small town drunk and drug addict, from being a piece of shit. I wanted a clear mind, a strong body, good name. I wanted to start fresh somewhere nobody knew my name. I wanted to learn what a fatherless boy misses out on, like how to be a man. I wanted to travel the world and learn about different cultures and landscapes. I wanted to go to Germany. I wanted to inhale fresh bread on cobblestone streets and eat pizza in Italy. I wanted a steady paycheck. I wanted to help the world, help my family, and help myself.

Such thoughts passed as I stared at the proud soldier on top of the stairs, the proudest man I ever saw. I wanted to hold my head high like him instead of hiding in alleys with my eyes down. I walked up the stairs without thinking and passed framed photographs of state champion athletes on the wall, hypnotized by badges and boots. He looked me in the eye with respect, shook my hand, and made me feel like the man I thought I was. Within minutes he had named a dozen countries he had visited within the past five years and when I told him that I wanted to be stationed in Italy as an airborne infantryman, he laughed and said: "There are more gorgeous women in a tiny coastal village in Italy than all of California." Then he elbowed me. "And, let me tell ya, they love Americans." He winked.

A couple of weeks later, I was on a bus with a handful of other young enlistees headed to Anchorage. We were given our hotel rooms downtown with meal tickets for the restaurant. That evening after dinner, I walked Fourth Avenue, watching drunk white people pick on drunk natives, I was so tired of being drunk. I returned to the hotel and felt like royalty; I stayed up late watching cable in bed. The next morning after breakfast, I went to the enlistment station for mandatory testing. And since I had mastered the habit of not trying on tests, and always envisioned a soldier as a lean, mean fighting machine, I was the first one finished, and by the end of the day, I chose the only job that I thought mattered in the army; airborne infantry, all the way.

"Sign here, here, here, and here... oh, and here, here, and here." A recruiter ripped two pages while flipping so fast and pointing. I signed as fast as I could. "You also need to sign here, here, here, and here; oh, and your initials right here, on these three lines." He kept his eyes down.

I squinted to read the tiny print at the bottom of the final page.

"Hold on a second," I said. "Why does this say eight years, when I'm enlisting for four?"

"Where?" He acted dumb.

"Here," I said, pointing.

He glanced at the American flag on the wall and took a deep breath.

"Don't worry about that," he said. "Your active duty time is matched by individual ready reserve time. Nobody gets called up for IRR."

"What does that mean?" I said.

He took another deep breath, "You're fucking worried, ain't ya, Stark." He laughed. "And I took you to be some kind of badass." I looked at him, confused. "It says here that you want to be airborne infantry, you do know that they're the toughest guys in the army. I'm starting to doubt that you could even handle it."

I clenched my jaw. "I'm going to show everybody who doubted me that they were wrong," I said.

"Don't worry about a thing," he said, patting my shoulder from across the desk. "The army will take care of you, I promise."

As the pen hovered above the final initial I thought about how proud my family would be; I pictured James pacing in solitary confinement, my mother sitting at the hotel lobby desk, and Victor studying the Quran. I could not picture my real father but thought he would be proud of me for doing something other than drinking. I recognized my lack of options.

"Where is your first duty station?" The recruiter asked, breaking my thought.

"Italy, sir," I said. "I've always wanted to visit."

"Don't call me, sir." He smiled. "I work for a living. Italy is beautiful," he said. "There are more gorgeous women in a tiny coastal village in Italy than all of California." I thought I had heard that line before. "And let me tell ya," he winked, "they love Americans."

Images of wine and women flashed in my mind. Pizza, architecture, sculptures, art, gondolas, canals, cathedrals, and romance...oh, the fucking romance! Venice! Verona! Rome! Florence! Milan! The Alps! Backyard vineyards overflowing with grapes. Tight-bodied babes with straight black hair on nude beaches. And an enlistment bonus of nine thousand dollars that could certainly help my mother out. I could do my own thing for a while, carve my path. I lowered the pen and initialed. It was done. Five days after graduation I would drive north without a plan to return. I would ship out to Fort Benning, Georgia for basic training, advanced infantry training, and airborne school. The recruiter patted my shoulder, shook my hand, and led me to a room with fifty flags and framed photographs of people I did not know or care about to recite an oath to protect my country against all enemies, foreign and domestic.

I returned to Seward with hope for the future and pride. Bruce could not believe my decision.

"After 9/11?" he said. "You'll have to go to war."

"So what," I said. "I'm a fucking warrior."

He thought I was crazy. Maybe I was; hell, maybe I still am. At least I found a way out. He brought me into the woods with a twenty-two to kill a squirrel. I held the gun with shaky hands and thought about the ptarmigan and the eternal spirit before lowering the gun.

"Why would I kill something that is not trying to kill me?" I asked.

"My dad had to kill all kinds of people in Vietnam," he said, "whether they tried to kill him or not. Why do you think he stays in his room all the time and beat the shit out of us?"

I gulped.

I compare every achievement in life to the reaction received in Mosul in April of 2003 when thousands of Iraqis crowded the streets to cheer our arrival. There were so many we could barely move the Humvees. They tossed cartons of cigarettes in the bed of our truck and offered us food, chai, and daughters. I was surprised by the reaction, and by the number of beautiful young women. The only pictures I had seen of Iraqi women showed them obese scowling at the camera.

"This is why we are here, boys," said Sully, standing behind the fifty. "To liberate these people from oppression."

We were all silent. A tear ran down Alvarez's face, Brammer smiled, I, too, wiped tears. A crowd of brown hair, brown eyes, and brown skin, I had never loved brown so much. They held signs that read, "We Luv Bush!" and "We Luv Amrika!" While waving tiny American flags. "Thank you, Mista!" they shouted. I felt like a real American hero. I was helping people, doing what I enlisted to do. We continued south with dozens of cartons of smokes and one hell of a morale boost.

In Kirkuk, we occupied an abandoned Republican Guard base with bunkers full of explosives and surface-to-air missiles pointed at the sky. We patrolled the city streets non-stop. Days dragged into weeks, and the next thing I knew it was May and I had not bathed with anything but baby wipes since before we parachuted in, in March. Morale plummeted. We quit asking when we would leave, nobody knew. Ringworm infested the platoon. We shaved our heads to prevent it and did laundry in buckets. One soldier had an especially hard time sleeping, he swore that he was hearing something crawl inside his head. We thought we had another Loveall on our hands until he returned from sick call with an inch-long beetle that was living in his ear. We slept in watch caps after that.

A telephone was put in operation and soldiers stood for hours in the sun while waiting for a fifteen-minute call home. With a twelve-hour time difference to Alaska, it was always an odd time to call, but Mother and Elliot always answered when I did. I didn't understand why Elliot answered, especially after I broke up with her when she left for college—but I was thankful. I listened to them talk about their lives while trying to forget my own. Mother had moved to Juneau after Victor was transferred from Spring Creek to Lemon Creek. She started working at Safeway and found a small mother-in-law cabin to rent. She enjoyed living in the capital city. Elliot had returned to Seward and started working at the restaurant where I used to work as a busser to save money for a trip to Thailand. I didn't talk about what I was doing, I had so much to say I didn't know where to start.

Eventually, non-combat arms personnel arrived on base and our company moved into the city to occupy abandoned buildings, sleep on cold sand and concrete, and rotate on the truck's wooden benches. Debaser and Hollywood kept the front seats warm. Our first sergeant chanted, "Sleep light, freeze tonight," and "Stay alert, stay alive," and they became my mantras and way of living.

Sleep deprivation, burnout, and dysentery were common. We were issued a single bottle of water and MRE per day. The water became so hot we could barely drink it. I lost weight, we all did, and we continued patrolling. We shut down roads and villages to search house to house and car to car hunting for Saddam and former soldiers of the Republican Guard. I began to feel like we weren't helping the people but terrorizing them. Pop shots were taken at us while on patrol became regular. Sweat and sand stained and stiffened our uniforms until they were so crisp they stood on their own. My thighs were chaffed, my feet peeled, and my body burned with prickly heat; it hurt to be alive. My face was a rash from dry shaving, my bowels plugged from dehydration and MREs, and my privates felt and smelled rotten. The worst part though was feeling forgotten. I was broken-hearted and lonely in time to celebrate my nineteenth birthday.

One mission we had for weeks was to chase looters

around an open-air cement factory as they tried to escape with supplies to rebuild their bombed-out homes. I felt for them, they were merely trying to reuse and recycle, but we were given strict orders to stop the looting. As we entered the compound bumper to bumper, our trucks broke off in different directions to chase people sprinting in terror. When we were within a few feet, drivers came to a screeching halt and those in the back jumped out to chase on foot. It was like a first-person shooter until I touched real-life people. Some stopped and raised their hands, others were tackled and pinned to the ground as we used zip ties to flex cuff their wrists behind their backs then yank an empty sandbag over their heads. The men were loaded in the truck bed shaking on the metal floor. We shoved them and told them to shut up while laughing and joking about our missed tackles. I didn't like doing it, but had to make light of it—they were orders. After every truck was full, we brought them to a detainment facility on base in Kirkuk and never saw them again.

One particular day, we chased an old man who was dragging a piece of sheet metal behind his tractor with a long chain. He stopped and raised his hands in surrender before hitting the gas and putting away. I admired his fearlessness.

"Do not fire!" ordered Hollywood from the passenger seat. "I repeat, do not fire!"

Debaser accelerated and pulled in front of the tractor. I pointed my weapon at the old man's face and he turned the tractor just in time to avoid a collision, heading into a busy neighborhood.

Eventually, he stopped again and turned to stare deep into my eyes as if saying: "You invaded my land, bombed my cities, destroyed my home, and killed my family. What more can you do?"

We dismounted and jogged at him with rifles pointed at his face. When we were within a few feet from the tractor, he slammed it in gear and slowly drove away.

"Mother fucker," I shouted, sprinting back to the truck.

The old man drove in circles on the edges of the factory as Hollywood shouted, "Don't fire! Do not fire!" Then, pop, pop, pop, Hollywood fired a three-round burst at a tire and missed. The old man stopped.

"Dismount, dismount, dismount," he yelled.

We ran at him with our weapons pointed at his face, and again, when we were within a few feet, he put the tractor in gear and crept away. It took every bit of self-restraint not to shoot him in the back of the head, I was so hot and dirty and full of rage. Locals stood outside laughing and pointing, which made me angrier. We ran back to the truck and climbed over the tailgate, but before I was in my seat on the wooden bench, Debaser hit the gas and I was flung forward with my upper body hanging over the tailgate, holding my rifle in my fingertips. Brammer and Alvarez grabbed my ankles to keep me from falling, and in slow motion, my rifle fell to the ground.

"Stop the fucking truck," yelled Sullivan. "Stop the fucking truck!"

Debaser kept chasing the tractor as my rifle became a

blip in the dust. I thought about how embarrassing it would be to be killed by my weapon, or even worse, to have my brothers killed.

"Stop the fucking truck!" he yelled again, slamming the top of the cab with his fist.

Debaser slammed the brakes and we skidded to a halt as the tractor continued toward the neighborhood. The tortoise and the hare, I thought. They released my ankles and I fell forward, rolled, and ran harder than ever before. Locals stared, a man pointed at my rifle and walked towards it. I was an alien invader from another planet, yelling "mother fucker" at the top of my lungs to scare the man. He stopped. Sweat ran down my body; my helmet, vest, 5.56 rounds, and grenades seemed to weigh thousands of pounds. I grabbed the rifle, pointed it at the man who winced and held up his hands then sprinted to the truck as it backed up. I climbed in to continue chasing the tractor.

A call for backup came over the radio. An Iraqi had been shot and needed evacuation. I watched the old man escape, happy about his victory. We raced to the other Humvees where an Iraqi man was lying on his back on the ground bleeding from a hole in his throat. His brother wailed and prayed and held his head in his bloody hands. His skin was gray, blood pooled in the sand beside him. Gravity took control. The dying man had tears running down his face, he was younger than I am now, crying as I write this. Foran killed him, the son of a bitch, he was smiling and leaning against a Humvee smoking.

"I was aimin' two inches over his head," he said, smirking and shrugging.

We loaded the man in a Humvee and rushed to base, but he was dead on arrival. Foran filled sandbags for a week as punishment for murder while my step-father was in prison for life. I was confused; my purpose and attitude were ruined. Everybody was a threat, including myself.

Eventually, Debaser was promoted to staff sergeant and moved to another company. He was replaced by an ex-UFC fighter who smoked cigars, collected and painted tiny Warhammer models, and kept to himself. We urged the short, stocky sergeant to grapple with our LT, who had helped design the army model of hand-to-hand combat and was easily the best grappler in the company, but UFC always said the same thing.

"I'm done with hand to hand," he said. "No more fighting for me."

"Then why the hell did you join the infantry?"

"Because combat is nothing like professional fighting," he said. "It is the difference between sport fishing and subsistence."

We played a joke on new guys who were sent in to replace the injured by having them wake up UFC by touching him. They would creep over to his bunk while Brammer, Sully,

Alvarez, and I watched from the other side of the room, and the moment they laid a hand on him, UFC would wake up kicking and swinging like a maniac. He gave one cherry a black eye and broke another one's nose. It was hilarious. He didn't like the new guys, but he liked the four of us. Of course, he never said it, but he did share his Dominican cigars to smoke on guard or between missions. Two cigars could last a twelve-hour guard shift.

Since our lieutenant was undefeated, he consistently challenged UFC by making comments outside of his humble character in hopes of making the dream of beating a professional fighter a reality. One day, UFC calmly set his paintbrushes on his cot, stood from his models, and said, "Okay, sir, now's the time." The platoon followed hooting and hollering. "The time has finally come to give you what you want, sir."

The two men were in the middle of a circle of hollering GIs, their dog tags dangling and brown t-shirts over BDU bottoms dirty. When they shook hands, a look of ferocity came over UFC's pale face like nothing I had seen. Probably because our firefights were always in the dark. He shot low and took the LT to the ground and within seconds had him in an arm-bar so tight the LT pleaded to be released. Everybody hollered. UFC squeezed tight and released, squeezed tight and released, as the LT groaned in pain. UFC, without a sign of strain on his face or voice, calmly said, "See sir, there is always somebody badder," then he let him go. The enlisted guys cheered and patted UFC on the back and we all took the opportunity to talk trash to the LT, who didn't show any signs of anger or disappointment just plain surprise. Without another word, UFC walked past everybody to his cot to light a cigar and finish painting a mini mjollner dark red.

Another time, we tied an MRE to a rope and dragged it behind our Humvee as barefoot children appeared from alleys and homes to chase it. They yelled, "Mister" and "Give me," the only words they knew. The only word we knew in their language was "Ishta" which meant, "back the fuck up." Dozens of kids laughed and chased the brown bag, some came within a few inches of grabbing it. We laughed with them, we laughed together. It felt good to laugh, especially after pointing my gun at so many scared faces while being terrified. Our body armor and loaded magazines rose and fell with our laughing hearts. Even local men smiled from their gated entryways. Women covered in clothing stared with smiling eyes, they dare not smile. Everybody smiled together. We pulled the string when kids got close and sped up to watch them sprint. Eventually, the fun ended when a group of kids with third-degree burns and a blown-off hand approached for medical care. They had been playing with unexploded ordinances. Our medic applied ointment and gauze and then gave them directions to a hospital that was so overcrowded we had to rotate guard shifts to keep people from overrunning the place. Who knows what came of them kids?

For days we had been searching villages for Saddam and other Republican Guard soldiers. I was exhausted, hungry, thirsty, and guilty from kicking in so many doors and pointing my rifle at so many faces. My squad searched a backyard and noticed a child covered with elephantiasis wearing a thick chain and collar staked to a sturdy post. He stared at us in wonder as we stared at him in horror. I thought of Marlena. Nobody spoke. He crawled inside a doghouse and spilled a bowl of water on the sand. Dozens of residents in that town had elephantiasis, and we guessed that it was something in the water. We refused chai and refrained from filling metal bowls kept in their freezers with tap water, which we typically did while searching houses. I wondered if the locals thought of me worse than they thought of the boy.

My platoon was voted as having the worst living conditions in the military at the time by the newspaper, The Stars and Stripes. A reporter came out to do an article and left the next day. It was July, an average of 130 degrees Fahrenheit. We lived at a water treatment facility where sand fleas, camel spiders, and scorpions terrorized us as we slept on the ground without shade. We were within stone's throw from the Tigris River where we bathed once a week as pop shots came from the other bank. Nothing was funny, besides the irony of being at a water treatment facility but still not having enough drinking water. Our only escape from the heat was an underground control room down a winding flight of crumbling concrete stairs where sometimes twenty guys huddled together to watch Chris Farley movies on a four-inch mini DVD player.

A few guys in another platoon were injured during an enemy ambush. And the following day, we ambushed and killed three Iraqis and stacked their bodies while some of the guys pissed on them and took pictures. I didn't do either. It was okay to kill people but unethical to deface them. We hid the bodies under a poncho in the back of the chow truck and laughed as we imagined the terror on the cooks' faces when they unloaded the empty food containers and found the dead bodies. We never talked about it again after that day.

Bruce did not enlist as he had promised, instead, he sent a small package with nothing but empty Starburst wrappers and a note.

"Sorry about the wrappers, I got high and ate all of the Starbursts. Check inside the wrappers."

Inside a pink wrapper was a dense green bud that I smoked out of a pop can on the roof with a couple of guys. Ten minutes later, celebratory tracers flew overhead and we hit the rooftop laughing. Tracers erupted across town, and we laid on our bellies whispering, "Holy shit."

UFC came upstairs found us and told us to gather our gear. Somebody was placing an IED under a bridge and we had to stop them. With eyes down, I nervously gathered my gear, then silently loaded into the back of the truck as Brammer and Sully remarked on how quiet I was. I was shaking as we drove toward the bridge, confused at how Vietnam Veterans could have smoked and done drugs while being at war and still been on top of their game. Luckily, nobody was at the bridge. I gave the rest of my bud to somebody else and didn't smoke again for years.

11

We called the road the Highway to Hell because we never knew if we would make it back, and we all knew where we were going when we died. It was the road that connected my platoon with the first platoon, the road we drove a few times every week to resupply them. The first platoon manned a traffic control point and guard tower at an old fort an hour's drive from our company's location where they rotated between pulling perimeter security and searching vehicles at a traffic control point. I don't remember how long they were there, it must have been a month or so, they had it rough though, I remember that. To top off their extra-long workdays, they had consistent mortar attacks which kept them from sleeping at night. We delivered them hot chow, bottled water, and mail at least twice a week, otherwise, they lived on MREs and care packages. The rest of Alpha Company ate chow that was delivered almost daily and *hajji* food we bought from the markets. We had been in country for ten or eleven months at that point without leave and we were pissed off, tired, and lonely. We were blown up so often on the Highway to Hell it was a given that every time we drove it we would make contact. Yet still, my heart raced and trigger finger danced, prepared for the ghosts on the roadsides who only attacked at night.

After finding an open valley with thousands of unexploded ordinances strewn about, my platoon worked for weeks loading our trucks with mines, mortars, bullets, and whatever else exploded and stacking them in huge piles inside abandoned tanks then covering them with dozens of sticks of C-4, lighting the fuse and driving far enough away to watch the explosion. It was a blast. Despite exposure to depleted uranium, it was a fun mission—a good break from searching houses, searching cars, and terrorizing people; although dry, hot and dirty—it would have been a lot better with more than a single bottle of water. It was also a little scary because we never knew if the rounds would explode, so we handled them very gently. Well, most of us… One soldier had a stack of mines in his lap that he rested his chin on with his eyes closed as we drove over bumpy dunes. Nothing happened.

One time we brought two EOD guys with us on the Highway to Hell, the soldiers who detonate bombs before they detonate us, I didn't understand why they came—we had been doing all the work ourselves, but I was just a private, and not meant to understand anything. After our explosion, we drove back to our safe house to grab the first platoon's supplies and then drive them out to them. Along the way, we spotted an IED on the roadside that was daisy-chained to three others, so we pulled security while EOD disarmed three 155 mm mortar rounds perfectly spaced 25 meters apart, just like our vehicles in the convoy. The enemy had become so advanced during my first tour that they knew our convoy spacing and began using bigger explosives to cause more damage. We left the first platoon's fort after dark, and let me tell you—it got really cold in the backs of our trucks at night—and somebody had forgotten to move a strand of concertina wire from across the road that Roche drove over. The wire wrapped around the axle like a tourniquet and prevented the truck from moving. Being pitch black made it even more difficult to untangle, especially because a long row of *hajji* vehicles were on both sides of the road and it was witch's hour—when people typically started shooting. Luckily we had Brammer, who set to the task and untangled the mess without any lasting damage to the vehicle or his hands. We didn't have time to eat that day other than a couple of snacks we brought from our care packages, so we were thirsty, hungry, cold, and tired, which made us irritable as fuck. All I wanted to do was get back to my cot to continue reading "The Shining."

The stars were shining, which always made it hard not to stare off and wonder if other beings on other planets fought and killed each other over natural resources and power. I hoped they were more advanced than us. My thoughts of Elliot had faded since she stopped answering my phone calls and writing me letters, she was dating somebody else now.

I thought of James, wondering how he was doing in prison and when he would get out. And of my mother. When I was almost asleep, I noticed a fireball on the left side of the road flying in slow motion at our truck.

"RPG!" yelled Brammer from behind the gun.

It flew a few inches over the hood and was followed by two more that bounced off the road between our trucks into darkness. AK-47 rounds exploded from both sides of the road as tracers flew over, under, and around us. We fired at the source as UFC sped through the kill zone.

"Make it stop, make it stop," cried a new guy.

"Shut the fuck up, you bitch," said Brammer. "And fire your fucking gun."

When the firefight was over and we were sitting in silence with that euphoric feeling that comes over you when you realize you are alive and unwounded and you don't know whether to thank God or count your lucky stars, one of the EOD guys laughed and said:

"It's a good thing that RPG didn't hit us," and he patted three crates of C-4. "Because we would all be dead."

When we made it back to our safe house in Tuz, Sully laid on his cot under an American flag reading: "How the Irish Saved Civilization." Alvarez joined the Hispanics to play cards and speak Spanish. UFC painted models and smoked. Sergeant Milton, our new squad leader who replaced Hollywood, and Brammer went downstairs to hit free weights—legal steroids had become popular and some of the guys got huge in weeks. I lay on my cot writing before reading and the new guy went outside. I wrote in the third person about the events that happened as a way to distance myself.

The next morning, UFC pulled shards of glass from his neck with pliers from his multitool. Nobody remembered where the glass came from.

"You could get a purple heart if you went to sick call and had them do it," said Milton, who already had one purple heart from an IED that exploded his truck and left him wandering around the center of the road with a bloody face as we lit up a village.

"People lose limbs to earn a purple heart," said UFC. "I won't disgrace them."

Nobody could find the new guy. He returned mid-morning walking unbalanced and acting deaf with his head leaning to one side. The medics at sickbay said the explosion had set off his equilibrium, and since it could not be tested in-country, he had to return to America. We were happy to see him go.

Almost every time we drove the Highway to Hell we were ambushed. Nobody died on our side, I never watched an American die, but we were scared as hell every time. Brammer and I had become bad luck charms because we were there every time our platoon was hit. It became a running joke that if somebody was getting bored and wanted action, they could come on patrol with us. One Doc had a huge chunk of his hand blown off in the same IED where Kershner got a chunk of shrapnel in the ass. Many of the guys took shrapnel and glass to the face, there were many concussions, near misses, scrapes, cuts, but that isn't to say that we walked away without injuries. During the writing of this book, I went through old journals and noticed month-long gaps between entries; all of my memories and entries are muddled and seemingly coded. It is hard to tell what is fact and what is fiction. I went through my memories and those of a couple of comrades to try and piece together our deployment. I sent the war chapters of this book to Brammer for suggestions who called and said, "Fat Bob," I had earned the nickname after he caught me stealing his pudding in the middle of the night. "I can't believe you remember these things so well…" he said. "Tell me that you wrote about our time in _____?"

"What are you talking about?" I asked. "Where?"

"You know," he said, "the weeks we spent in _____. They were our hardest weeks. Tell me you wrote about that."

I hesitated, reminded of the feeling after a blacked-out night of drinking, I was embarrassed to say it.

"I don't know what you're talking about," I said. "I don't remember any of it."

Eventually, my platoon was given an order to find and kill the Highway Bandits. Not only were they shooting at us, but they were also killing and robbing locals too. So we set up an observation post on a hill overlooking the road and we were told not to return until we killed or detained the enemy. We packed our trucks with enough supplies for two weeks. It was some time in January or February, when it was so cold we shivered and wore neck gaiters during the day. We could see our breath. I missed home, I was tired of being in the desert and ready to return to the mountains, forest, tundra, and water.

Alvarez volunteered to stay awake watching the road through a thermal device called a Clue, while the rest of us lay on the ground trying to stay warm. Not more than thirty minutes after dark, Alvarez called for UFC.

"I see people on the road, sergeant," Alvarez whispered.

"Let me see the Clue," said UFC.

Shuffling came from sleeping bags, I wasn't the only one who couldn't sleep. The anticipation and silence were too much to sleep through.

"There were three of them," said Alvarez, "maybe four."

Sullivan, Brammer, and I had our boots on and sleeping bags packed in our hanging rucks within seconds, without a sound, listening to Alvarez and UFC on the back of the truck.

"I'll be damned," said UFC. "You're not pulling my leg, Alvarez. Hey, Milton, LT, *hajji* is definitely on the road."

LT and Milton climbed in the truck to take turns looking.

"Shine your PEQ-2 down there," said LT, referring to a laser that we used to aim at night that can only be seen with night vision goggles.

"Put it on their heads," said Milton.

Adrenaline surged, and I went from exhausted to alert within seconds. Sully, Brammer, and I put chews in our lips and nodded to each other.

"The motherfuckers ducked," said UFC. "They fucking ducked!"

"Shine it in front of them and see what happens," said LT.

I waited anxiously for the response.

"They turned around," said Milton. "The mother fuckers turned around."

"They must have night vision," said LT. "Or they couldn't see the laser."

"*Hajji* is equipped," said UFC.

"They're on the other side of the road now," said Alvarez.

"What do you think, LT?" Said UFC. "Do we get 'em?"

There was a pause, a long pause.

"Let's wait and see what happens," said LT. "We don't want to kill the wrong guys."

"Roger sergeant," said UFC.

After a few minutes of nervous silence, headlights appeared on the road from a car traveling east on the highway until they slowed down and came to a complete halt. Gunfire erupted from both sides of the road, lighting up the vehicle.

"Get the fuck up," yelled Milton. "We have four or more *hajji* on the road and we need to get the fuck down there."

We were in the truck within seconds ripping down the hill toward the highway. Cold air whipped my face yet I felt only heat.

"Let's end these motherfuckers," said Alvarez.

One vehicle stayed on the hill as overwatch while the other three went for it. By the time we reached the road, the people in the car were dead, and whoever had done it had disappeared.

"They're laying down just south of the road, over," said a soldier on the radio from the overwatch position.

With my truck in lead, we searched the roadside fields full of bumps and holes. We bounced all over the place trying to keep our eyes steady. I could feel the eyes of the enemy on us but could not see them.

"Those guys on the hill must be seeing snakes," said Alvarez, "'cause there ain't a damn thing out here."

Please don't blow us the fuck up or pop up and shoot us, was all I could think. I knew that if they did, they may kill one or two of us before quickly being overpowered. The adrenaline high wore off after a few minutes and I became so tired I almost fell asleep. I was losing hope, a sinister, barbaric hope to find and kill the people who had been trying to kill us. I wanted to blow their fucking brains out and put an end to the fear. We bounced around the field barely idling. I fell asleep and began to snore and Brammer shoved me and told me to wake the fuck up.

I thought about a shepherd whom we met a couple of weeks prior who was all alone minus hundreds of sheep out in the hills miles away from any dwellings. He had told our interpreter, "This is Iraq, there is no hope for us." So why was I risking my life and the lives of fellow Americans for people who didn't even believe in their own country's future?

"Here comes another vehicle, over," said the voice on the radio. "Sit back and wait, over."

We sat in silence with our lights off, waiting. As the vehicle got closer, the gunmen fired from the road and our drivers turned on their headlights and drove straight at the road until our wheels hit the asphalt and we flew towards the gunfire. I flipped the safety on my grenade launcher and rifle and took a deep breath. We went up and over a small hill until a truck appeared in the center of the road twenty meters to our front. Tracers erupted from both sides, from the truck and from where the car was, and we screeched to a halt with all three vehicles in line. The big guns roared as I dismounted like I had thousands of times and knelt beside the truck firing.

"Die mother fuckers, die!" yelled Alvarez with both fingers pressed down on the butterfly trigger of the fifty calibers.

We all yelled. We hated them and wanted them dead.

I had a running competition with UFC to see who could fire the most grenades during our firefights. It was a way to turn fear into fun. And I must say, I won that night, launching nineteen to his thirteen.

Two *hajji* used the truck as cover as they fired at us, I was amazed they were still alive, so I lobbed a grenade and hit the truck. It exploded and caught fire, the men stopped shooting. We cheered. I was pleased with my aim. Milton shot from behind the Humvee door while yelling at us to get behind cover, the only problem was that there wasn't any cover. Brammer was on his belly to my right with his squad automatic weapon going through hundred-round drums like chewing tobacco. His gun began to run, which is when the bullets keep firing and firing without a break, and in a panic, he lifted the butt-stock and pointed the barrel at the ground as chunks of asphalt sprayed in my face and I thought I was hit but it didn't matter because I wasn't dead. What mattered was to keep firing until they stopped. That's it, the simple life. After who knows how long, the enemy's bullets stopped and we continued until two men held up their arms by the car and Lieutenant Spencer yelled: "Ceasefire! Ceasefire!" And the order was echoed as blood, adrenaline, and everything else that a person can feel surged through my body.

"Pop a loom!" said Milton. I removed an illumination round from my grenade vest, put it in the tube, and launched it high. UFC did the same, followed by other grenadiers. We could see the surrounding fields and highways.

"Follow me!" yelled LT. "Follow me!"

He walked toward the flaming truck with buttstock to cheek as Brammer and I picked up without hesitation and formed a tight wedge behind him, ready to shoot anything that moved. Please don't move, please don't move. We passed by two dead guys outside of the truck walking toward two crying men on the left side of the road. We approached them with our barrels in their faces, grabbing their underarms and yanking them onto the road.

"Shut the fuck up!" I yelled.

The headlights from our trucks were followed by more luminary rounds so we could see. We found three more dead on the left before crossing the road.

"Sergeant Milton," said LT over his radio, "get an extinguisher on the truck, over."

I heard the sound of extinguishers behind me and could tell the fire was being put out by the dimming light. Brammer and I assembled the wounded in the same area to watch them, forgetting the rule of separating them. They wailed. Our medic was left on the hill in the overwatch vehicle, so Brammer and I administered first aid to bullet and shrapnel wounds. The soldier who couldn't shit and then shit his pants volunteered to pull guard on the detainees. He loved pulling guard on detainees. We found multiple sets of night vision goggles while searching them, then pulled security for two hours while listening to them cry.

Robert Stark

A brand new battalion commander had arrived replacing Lieutenant Colonel Tunnel after he was shot in a firefight and sent home. The new commander wanted to win the hearts and minds of the Iraqis, so he arrived with an entourage of clean soldiers with pressed uniforms, fat bodies, and soft eyes.

"Give me a fucking chew," I said to the colonel's driver. "Now…"

"But you have blood all over your hands," he said.

"I don't give a fuck. Just give me a fucking chew."

He opened his can and held it out while I put my bloody fingers in it and filled my lip.

"Keep the can," he said.

"Give me one of those," said Brammer, whose hands were also covered in blood. "Blood or not, I need a fucking dip."

"You guys are savages," said the driver. And we stared at him with red eyes. "What the hell happened to you guys out here?"

Brammer and I looked at each other, smiled, and laughed hysterically.

13

It was February 19, 2004, not quite eleven months after parachuting into Iraq. Alpha Company 1/508th Infantry stood inside the Newark airport staring at the skyline of New York City, where the twin towers had been.

"I wish they'd just let me go home," said Alvarez. "I can practically see my neighborhood in Yonkers. It's crazy to think that I'm only forty-five minutes from my parents."

Specialist Reed came up and patted my shoulder. "You were right," he said.

"About what?"

"I made it home with my dick." He grabbed himself and laughed while two guys only a few years older than us walked by in business suits shaking their heads in disapproval. We left America and arrived at a hangar full of people in Aviano, Italy. I watched their hands and faces, ready to shoot. Back at Camp Ederle in Vicenza, the duty station I had so badly hoped for when I enlisted less than two years prior, Joan Jett sang, "I Love Rock and Roll" in a massive tent where families gathered to eat barbecue. Brammer, Sully, and I went to the liquor store. We returned to the barracks to change into civilian clothes for the first time since leaving, and within hours I was blacked out. Brammer, Sully, and I went to Germany for a weekend. It was just like mother had said, everybody seemed so happy and so different yet still the same, everybody but me. I couldn't help scanning, doorways, rooftops, shops, and people looking for guns and explosives. So I chose to drink from sunrise to sunset to ease my nerves. I bought a leather jacket and leather shoes for four hundred euros to feel better about myself until I saw myself in a shop window and realized how fake and superficial I was being so I left them next to a homeless person, thinking that maybe I could do something good for somebody. I had close to twenty-three thousand dollars in the bank, and it would all be gone within six months.

When I returned to Seward for leave, everything was just as I had left it, everything but me. Elliot's new man was gone fishing so she invited me to hang out on the beach to catch up.

"What is God but another symbol created to provide comfort and control?" I said.

"A three-letter word," she said. "God is just another three-letter word. Other than that, it means nothing." We watched the moon rise over Mount Alice while a cacophony of seagulls bobbed on the water. Her eyes twinkled like mirrors to the stars and she smelled better than I imagined.

"I just don't understand the hype about this fucking God character," I said. "Too many innocent people die for no fucking reason. One side prays to God and another side does the same thing, and then they kill each other. It doesn't make any fucking sense."

"Please calm down," she said, touching my shoulder. "It doesn't matter, now. You are here, in Seward. Everything is cool." I revolted from her touch.

"None of it makes sense," I said, lighting another cigarette. "Here we are staring at the moon while people in other places are too afraid to go outside. Does God love America more than other countries?"

She put her on my shoulder again and said that everything would be okay.

"Runaway with me," I said. "Please... please... I can't stand the idea of going back. I know you're with so and so but we can go south of the border and hide out. I can't go back and terrorize those people, I just can't."

She shook her head. "Let's be together right now," she said. "Don't worry about the future."

"Yeah, that's easy for you to say," I said. "You work in a god damn photo lab and have a boyfriend who makes a ton of money." I continued to chain smoke in silence, it was something I had picked up. She kept her hand on my shoulder without a word. My old friends wanted to hang but I couldn't stand being around them. All they did was laugh and joke and they were never serious. Elliot asked me to stay the night and we lay on the couch cuddling watching *The Notebook*. She told me it was the story of us. "But in the end, they get married and live happily ever after," I said.

"Isn't it beautiful," she said.

"So does that mean you will run away with me?" I asked.

She pulled my arm over her until it was touching her breasts.

"Shh…" she said.

I begged her to go with me to Belize or Costa Rica or somewhere to start a family and live. She thought, shook her head, and said: "I can't leave Seward. This is where my family and friends are, where I grew up."

"They can visit," I said. "Everybody can visit."

"My dad would never go down there," she said. "And my mom would worry sick."

"I can protect you," I said. "I'm good at that, now."

"Protection from what?" she asked. "I don't need protection."

I didn't understand.

The next night we lay under the stars on a blanket staring at the moon. I could feel the tension in her body like she was holding back an ambush of questions she didn't know how to ask. I wished she would, I wished she wouldn't.

"You seem different, now," she said. "More serious; you've changed."

"I have," I said, smoking and laughing at a barrage of images from my tour. "I most definitely have changed. I just don't know how to tell you about it."

"I wish you would," she said.

"Maybe one day."

A shooting star flashed across the sky and I wished to not return to Iraq ever again.

J ust to set the record straight, I married my first girlfriend when I was twenty, maybe nineteen. We met up in Anchorage after I left Elliot in Seward because I needed more love and promises than she could give. It was the same girl I lost my virginity to in ninth grade before my mother moved to Seward and our entire family broke apart. Megan and I had met and started dating in seventh grade, wrote thousands of notes to each other, made out anywhere and everywhere, and defied her parents' wishes. They eventually tapped her phone and listened to Megan tell her best friend all about our sexual exploits. They demanded to meet my mother and me at a coffee shop appropriately named, Jitters, where they warned me to stay away from their daughter or have a restraining order issued. We did not talk again after I moved to Seward. Not until I came home on leave, and called her up. And we proceeded right where we had left off.

After six months in Italy, where I was such a bad

alcoholic I never made it to Rome, Milan, or Florence; I was transferred to Fort Campbell, Kentucky and I spent my 50 days of leave in Bend, Oregon where Megan was attending Central Oregon Community College. I paid her rent, bought groceries, weed, and alcohol, and had angry, violent sex. Her roommate accused her of stealing money, but she denied everything and accused her roommate of being an alcoholic. Her neighbors accused her of begging for pills but she denied everything and said they were lying.

I believed her. Why would she lie to me? And even if she did, I could tell, I was trained. We got engaged and planned to move to Kentucky together.

One day I cruised a bike down back roads past Newport Market, over a narrow, wooden bridge to the other side of the Deschutes River. I leaned against a ponderosa pine in Drake Park watching wood ducks swim with mallards. The ducks lowered their beaks to the river bottom with their feathered butts in the air. It was the cutest darn thing I had ever seen, and I watched them while smoking for hours.

This is not a joke, Bob, said the voice inside my head. Do you want to marry somebody who lies and steals from their best friend? You need more time—time away from Iraq and the trauma, you need to think about what you want to do with your life. I tossed a pebble in the river and watched ripples fade away then walked to Ranch Records and bought 'Rocket to Russia' by The Ramones.

You can't replace one girl with another and think she will just disappear, I thought. It doesn't work like that.

I rode the bike back to her house and walked in the front door.

She walked towards me with a piece of mail in her hand. "I need help," she said.

"What's the deal?"

"For some reason, I got a two hundred and fifty dollar phone bill," she said. "It doesn't make sense."

"Two-hundred and fifty dollars," I said. "Who have you been calling?"

"I haven't called anybody," she said. "It must have been somebody who came over for a party."

"People don't usually make long-distance phone calls from other peoples' houses," I said. "Let me take a look."

She handed me the mail. At least seven calls were made to the same number in Sebastopol, California, each one over an hour. I knew that her ex-boyfriend lived there, the guy she started dating when I moved to Seward and the two of them became addicted to pills together.

"What's the deal with the calls to Sebastopol?" I said.

"No clue," she said. "As I said, it must have been somebody from our last party."

I rubbed the handful of whiskers on my chin.

"I didn't realize that people make long-distance calls from other people's houses," I said. "What kind of friends do you have?"

"Oh, I don't know," she said. "They're just people. Can you help me pay for it? Please."

I looked at the bill and took a deep breath.

"I say we call to find out who is on the other end. We can pinpoint who made the calls and make them pay." I reached for the cordless phone. "What do you think?"

She tapped her foot. "Okay," she said. "Why not?"

I turned my back and dialed, knowing damn well whom I would find on the other line. The phone rang. It was quiet, everything happened in slow motion.

"Stop," she said. "Hang up the phone!" she grabbed the phone and slammed it into the charger.

"What the fuck are you doing?" I said.

"I need to tell you something," she said, her head down with watery green eyes.

"You're damn right you do," I said. "What's going on here?"

"I have to tell you a lot of things. I have been lying to you."

"So what your roommate and neighbors say is true? You are a liar and a drug addict? What else are you lying about?"

She shook her and cried. In a cold room with wood floors, she told me about her addiction to pills, and how she was still using but trying to quit. How was I so fucking stupid? I told her that I didn't want to be with her anymore, not as a boyfriend, a friend, and not as a husband. I left her house, rented a room in a hotel, and drank an entire bottle of whiskey while chain-smoking a pack of Marb 100s.

She had problems, I thought, serious problems.

The next morning, I returned to her place while she was in class to use the phone. I called about a Subaru station wagon with Alaska plates, and within a few hours, I owned my first car. I showed up after she was done with school to grab my duffel bag and say goodbye. She cried and begged for forgiveness, swearing that she would never lie again and would quit using pills for good but I didn't believe or forgive her. I called her a long list of terrible names, told her that I never wanted to see her again, then drove east to my birth town of Caldwell, Idaho.

What if she overdoses? I worried. It's not my fucking problem.

I visited my Great Uncle Smiley and Great Aunt Anita who fed me, let me bathe, and gave me a room to stay in. When my aunt went to bed, my uncle told me about his struggles after Vietnam but I didn't listen. Instead, I told him about Megan.

"The best thing a man can do is find a woman who will love him no matter what," he said. "And it sounds to me like you have quite a history with that young lady. You ought to go back and marry her."

The next day, we went to Walgreen's to fill his prescriptions and he wore a Vietnam Veteran hat covered in pins. Two people shook his hand and thanked him for his service, it made him glow. On the way home, he stopped in front of a dilapidated white house with peeling paint and mossy shingles.

"You know something, Bobby Joe," he said. "Some Starks used to live in that house, years ago. I'm not sure who lives in it anymore, but it might be worth stopping by."

"I don't know any of the Stark family," I said, "including my father. Maybe I'll come back later."

We ate turkey sandwiches and potato soup for lunch with sweet tea. Megan had called my mother for their number and called a half dozen times. I left in search of the dilapidated white house and became lost in the neighborhood. An hour later, I found it and parked on the opposite side of the road in a patch of dirt where a tire swing blew in the wind in a vacant lot as I walked to the front door.

Knock knock… I waited, there was no sound.

Knock knock… I listened, intently.

Knock knock knock…

I went to the next house. My heart pumped to the beat of an empty street with leaves blowing in the wind. I knocked three times before returning to the car.

"Where the fuck is everybody?" I lit a smoke and pondered the next move. I was high on nerves and emotions, so I decided to check one more house before abandoning all hope of meeting the Stark side.

The third house had a weathered white fence and a dandelion yard with a large window. I stood outside the gate, took a deep breath in preparation for disappointment, then lifted the creaky latch. An old woman stood and looked out the window, and I lowered the latch to wait. She opened the front door and stepped on the porch in a robe and slippers.

"Can I help you?" she said in a somewhat familiar voice.

"I am sorry to disturb you, ma'am," I said. "But I am looking for somebody."

"Who are you looking for?"

I took a deep breath. "I was told by an uncle that some

Starks used to live in the house two down from yours." I pointed. "I knocked—but nobody was home. So I went to the next house, but nobody was there either. So here I am…"

She took a pair of glasses out of a pocket in her robe and put them on. Looking at me intensely, she closed the door behind and said, "And who might you be?"

"My name is Robert Joseph Stark, ma'am. My mother is Sheri Lynn Moore and my father is Bertis Levi Stark."

She smiled and lifted her arms as her eyes filled with tears.

"Well, then," she said, walking down the stairs toward the gate. "That would make me your grandmother. Bert is my son. Come over here and give your grandma a hug."

I stood still, afraid, unbelieving. She opened the gate and hugged me and insisted that I follow her up the stairs. Inside, she showed me pictures of myself as a baby and pictures of my family that I had never seen.

"When was the last time you talked to your daddy?"

"We have never talked."

She stared in disbelief and shook her head.

"Let's change that. Your dad isn't good at staying in touch with people." She picked up the telephone and dialed.

To say I was nervous would be an understatement; I hoped he did not answer.

"You'll never guess who came knocking on my door and is now sitting on my couch," she said and a voice that sounded just like my brother came from the other end. "Your youngest son, Robert, is sitting here right now drinking lemonade." Shouting came from the other end. Things were happening so fast that I didn't have time to think. "Okay, okay," she said. "Go ahead and talk to him now, I'm sure you two have a lot of catching up to do." I stared at the phone. What the fuck would I say, "Thanks for never sending any birthday cards?" She pressed the receiver to my ear and a voice came through that sounded just like mine.

Our conversation was informal and uneventful, as most conversations were between strangers. Starter questions were bounced back and forth without diving into anything deeper. And after a few minutes, he had to deal with an urgent situation that required his full attention, so he had to go.

"What did he say?"

"Nothing; he apologized for not being around, and said that we are better off without him"

She shook her head.

"Your father has never been good at keeping in touch," she said. "He's a stranger to his mother. He left here over thirty years ago and I have only seen him once."

"At least now I know what his voice sounds like," I said.

"Yeah, it sounds just like yours." She smiled.

She invited over unknown family members who arrived within an hour. A woman and child who claimed to be my cousins; an uncle who collected records to sell on the internet gave me a stack; another uncle had missing teeth and long stringy hair; an aunt with straight black hair and Indian features had three sons. They had all been following the war and were worried sick about me, whereas I didn't even know they existed.

I returned to Uncle Smiley and Aunt Anita's after dark to chain smoke on the porch and then try to sleep. I was overwhelmed by the idea of having a family, I was so lonely and fucking scared. I didn't want to go to Kentucky or back to Iraq, I just wanted to get out of the Army and disappear. The next morning I called Megan and agreed to return to Bend. She promised that she would change while I thought I was perfect and didn't need to.

We went straight to the bedroom when I got there. She apologized and swore to stand by me no matter what. It went in one ear and out the other; I didn't need any fucking support, she did.

The next day we walked down a winding path through Drake Park on a mission to find a place to be married. We were denied at all of the churches and we left mocking them. "They don't know us, they're just a bunch of judgmental Christians."

At the courthouse, we were referred to a woman who married couples at home. And we pressed our ears to the phone and set an appointment for the next day. I called my mother and told her and she apologized for not being able to make it and wanted to make sure that I knew what I was doing. I was doing the right thing, I told her.

Megan called her parents who caught the red eye. The last time I had seen them was at Jitters when they threatened a restraining order, and they weren't pleased to see me. We met them at Megan's favorite diner and shook hands without smiling. I laughed and stared at her father. He was short and strong but I knew I could take him.

After breakfast, he brought me to GAP to buy a button-up shirt and slacks while the ladies went dress shopping. We didn't talk. The women picked him up and they all went back to the house to prepare. I would meet them at the address; I couldn't jinx the thing by seeing her dress before the ceremony.

I walked a couple of miles from the Old Mill District toward the west side, wondering if I was doing the right thing. I reminded myself that my aunt and uncle had known each other only a few weeks before they were married, and they had been together for over thirty years. Military life isn't so bad, I thought. I could stay in, but not if I have to do another tour in Iraq. Fuck that! Why are you thinking about war right now? I told myself. You're about to get married.

I had a hard time finding the house, but we arrived simultaneously. She seemed to float out of the car while I trudged through the mud. I could not believe she would marry a piece of shit like me. We held hands and walked inside, exchanging pre-made vows in the living room. Her father signed as a witness. Her roommate and neighbors did not come despite the invitation. Her parents brought us to a fancy restaurant and handed us an envelope with a thousand dollars. They bought us a hotel room, where I got so drunk I can't even remember the evening.

We drove east to Kentucky as a honeymoon, fighting and arguing the entire way.

We rented an apartment off base in Clarksville, Tennessee where she found a job at a cafe. I was jealous and did not want her to spend time with coworkers and make friends for fear that she would start using. I wanted her to quit and stay at home but she refused. I continued to drink every night to the point of blacking out. We went to bars to play pool but I was too young to drink legally so I didn't like going. We argued incessantly. Megan started smoking weed with a guy from work and I thought it meant they were having sex. She told me that I needed to slow down on drinking and I told her that she was the one with real problems. So I started frying chicken and making mashed potatoes to stay home and eat dinner together, it didn't work, we still fought. So I bought a new truck from the dealership, a pit-bull puppy, and vintage furniture from an auction, but nothing made me feel like I deserved love and trust. How could I forgive and trust her if I could not forgive and trust myself?

The arguments intensified, followed by aggressive sex. We went hiking and spotted an owl in a tree and then argued about what it meant to see an owl. She thought I needed to see a counselor to talk about the things that happened in Iraq, and when I did, the counselor told me that I needed medication for attention deficit disorder, so I walked out. I was beginning to think that maybe I was affected by my first tour. I hadn't talked about anything with anybody and planned to keep it all to myself... maybe it was time...

But then I started joking with her about divorce which led to serious discussions about the option. So when I was sent to Louisiana for training, she returned to Alaska with the puppy because I did not trust her alone. We talked over the phone and I continued to argue. I accused her of using and cheating; I threatened divorce and she said, "Fine, do it," and I told her that I always knew she wanted to get a divorce. So when I returned to Tennessee, I filed papers. I wired her a thousand dollars and refused to answer her calls. She hesitated to sign, she had meant her vows—she said over voicemail, I had not. Eventually, she signed, and we did not see or hear from each other for over ten years. Until we walked past each other at a music venue in Anchorage, turned around, and faced each other.

"It is nice to see you again," I said. She nodded, we hugged, and I went to the bathroom and left.

Two nights before my second deployment, two of my buddies were buying beer in a convenience store when I noticed a woman in a short red skirt with tube socks and a yellow tank-top, pacing back and forth. I approached her.

"Are you okay?" I said from six feet away.

"Yeah, why? What's up?" She stared down at the ground.

"I was watching you for a second," I said, "and you seem stressed. Everything all right?"

She lifted her head and revealed bright blue eyes in the gas station lights. She searched my eyes for intention. Her face was pale, pretty, and young and she couldn't be more than nineteen, I was twenty-one.

"Of course, I'm all right," she shrugged. "Why? Do I look like I'm not all right or something?"

"I just know that whenever I pace around it's because I'm not all right."

"Are you sure that's all you want from me?" she said. "To see if I'm all right."

I nodded and shrugged, "What the hell else would I want?"

She laughed, "I could think of a lot of things. I thought kindness only existed in fairy tales."

I shrugged, "I'm not a creep, but I'm not always kind, either." I thought back to my first year, to pointing my rifle at foreign faces while yelling at them to get outside of their home.

"It's hard to see past the shadows into the light," she said, straightening her back. "I could use a ride home. If you don't mind?"

"Where you headed?"

"Around the block," she said. "A few minutes away."

"We have to wait for my friends inside and then we can take off."

"Cool." She followed me to the Subaru and sat in the passenger seat. "I can't ever find good people. I'm only eighteen, yet I feel like I have lived hundreds of years."

"I know the feeling."

Her hair had streaks of purple, and she had scars on her forearms. She also had a large scar on her right thigh. While I tried not to look, it was too large to miss, and she had nice legs. My friends came outside, looked at her through the windshield, then at me, then at each other, they shrugged and got in the back seats. I turned to face them.

"We're going to give this lady a ride to her house," I said. "If that's cool with you guys."

They smiled and shrugged.

I followed her directions into a part of Clarksville that was banned from military personnel.

"Are you by any chance looking for a cheap blow job?" she said, breaking the silence.

I laughed nervously. "Excuse me?"

"Are you by any chance looking for a cheap blow job?"

Am I? I wondered. Hmmm…

"How much would it cost?"

"Depends what you want to pay."

"Less than twenty bucks," I said, out of curiosity.

"If you're that cheap," she said, "I could get you one for five."

"I didn't know it was possible to get a blow job for five bucks," I said.

"I have a toothless friend named, Martha," she said, "but, I have other friends, too."

She looked at me with those pretty blue eyes, licked her lips, and slightly parted her legs.

"Take this right," she said, "this right."

I made a sharp turn onto a dark street with flickering street lamps. I scanned my surroundings and noticed shadows everywhere. I wished I had a gun.

"I'm not sure that I want to pay for sex," I said. "At least, I don't think so."

"Slow down, slow down!" She touched my arm gently, it felt good. "My friends are willing to do other things, too," she said, "for less than a hundred. We're almost there, it's the next house on the left." We parked in front under watchful eyes.

"I'll be right back," she said, before running past shadows on a porch into the front door.

"You going to pay this girl for a BJ or what?" said one of the guys.

"Not tonight," I said. "At least, I don't think so."

"Why the hell not?" The other one said. "She is gorgeous."

"Oh, hell," I said. "I don't know." I thought about the year-long deployment we would be on in the next couple of days and how lonely the last one was. "I can't pay a young girl for sex," I said. "It would tear me apart, ethically."

"She's the same age as us! And besides, it's going to be a long year with just your hand."

"That's for sure," said the other.

"Just think," one of them said, "you could be paying for a child to eat."

I shook my head. "I don't want to think about that." I paused to watch the handful of black men on the porch staring at us. "What about you guys? It's not just me she's asking." They looked at each other, shrugged, then shook their heads. "Exactly," I said.

She ran to the car and climbed into the passenger seat.

"Let's go," she said. "Hurry!" I sped off. "Are you sure you don't want any pleasure this evening?" She turned around to ask my friends and I noticed her perky breasts and huge cleavage with strong perfume. The guys looked at each other, down to the ground, then out the windows. I assumed they were thinking the same thing I was. In two days we would be in Iraq surrounded by infantrymen for an entire year.

This could be our last chance to be with a woman, especially if we died.

They denied the offer.

"I don't blame you," she said. "When I used to hook, I charged more than a hundred dollars. I don't do it anymore, though, not after I had my baby girl."

I wondered where God was and why such things happen, about the possibility of reincarnation and karma. What could she have done to possibly deserve this life? We drove in silence for a few minutes before she asked, "Have you guys ever seen crack?"

I started laughing.

"What is so funny?"

"I didn't expect you to say that," I said.

"Well, have ya?" she said. I realized what she had in her fist and why we had gone to the shady house. Her skirt was higher than before and I could see her milky thighs.

"I have never seen crack," said one of the guys in the back.

"Me, neither," I said.

"I have," said the other. "And it's not something I like to be around."

The girl turned on the dome light and opened her hand, revealing a small black rock. It wasn't nearly as destructive looking as I imagined, it looked like a really hard ball of resin. The guys leaned forward to look.

"Do you smoke, or are you just getting it for friends?" I said.

She looked out the window.

"No, I don't smoke, not after having my baby girl," she

said. "I take care of her now, she changed my life. It's for friends who live with me."

I nodded and turned off the dome light as she continued to stare outside. At her house, she got out of the car without saying a word and walked to the front door without looking back. One of the guys got in the front seat and we went downtown to drink, laugh, and blackout while telling our friends about the girl. I don't even remember driving home with a carload of young men, but hell—I wasn't the one with a problem. It was everybody else.

I loaded a Blackhawk helicopter with an M-4 slung tightly over my chest and a 9 mm on my leg. My mission for year two in Iraq was private security for the commanding general of the 101st Airborne Division. Wherever he went, I protected him, rotating out with other guys from my platoon. We were flying with doors open to a meeting in Baghdad with two planned stops on the return trip. It wouldn't be a long day. He surprised me by sitting in the hell hole, where the wind hits your face so hard that nothing else exists, so I sat across from him. I did not understand why he chose the seat, and when I offered to take it, he refused. The wind and rotors were so loud that nothing was heard but the ringing in my ears. His old cheeks flapped in the wind and with his sunglasses on I couldn't tell if his eyes were open or closed, I imagined they were closed. What kind of stress is he dealing with? I wondered. My body was oriented out as I watched the vast flat desert pass below.

Endless miles of browns and tans; sand the color of dry grass in fall after going to seed. Yet I had come to learn that the dry Iraqi people were far from brittle. The ground was cracked in places; it had not rained for months and was always windy. It was like being in the Arctic Circle with only shrubs and small plants; minus the shrubs, small plants, and Arctic Circle. I wished I was home and out of the military. I wished I wouldn't have gotten married and divorced. I wished I would have never joined.

We flew over a tiny village with a handful of dwellings that were probably around before Christ, children played outside. Two of them waved, half a dozen fired invisible rockets and rifles. The general waved back, his old cheeks flapping in the wind, I waved too. Maybe he saw his grandchildren in them, I thought.

There was no mountains or water only endless sand in wavy, wind drift lines. We flew over a town with less than thirty dwellings and an open-air market. People stopped to watch the three helicopters fly over. Nobody waved. The general waved, so I did too.

In the middle of the desert, miles away from any village, cars, and trucks parked on the brown side of a line of white sand that stretched as far as I could see. Dozens of humans with baskets and tools were on foot in the white sand.

"They are gathering salt, sir, over," said the pilot in the headset.

The general nodded, looked at his green aviator gloves, then back outside.

Why did he sit there? I wondered. To meditate for a few moments?

We flew beside a highway riddled in potholes, over a traffic control point being manned by three Humvees, and a dozen American soldiers wearing *hajji* wraps over their faces as protection from whipping sand. Hundreds of vehicles waited in a wavy line that never stopped moving. The soldiers waved and the general waved back. It was like being private security for Tom Hanks.

Endless stretches of brown sand, power lines, highway, and stillness.

"Gunners, get ready, over."

The door gunners looked at each other, nodded, and smiled. I was excited. I had joined the army to travel and today I would visit Baghdad for the first time.

We flew over the outskirts where power lines, sheet metal, and people prevailed. Busy markets, shopping centers, schools, homes, vehicles; human existence was happening just like back home only on a larger scale and much faster. Baghdad is just like my mother's idea of Germany, I thought. Everybody just wants to be happy. Nobody waved, hardly anybody looked up. Smoke billowed from different parts of the city while a pack of dogs chased something around a street corner and mosque speakers chanted a prayer. It was a beautiful myriad of movements. An artist's dream, the juxtaposition of elaborate palace and mosque with ancient building techniques and standards of living. I wanted to land and walk around the city without a gun and uniform but knew it was an impossibility. Maybe in the future, I told myself, I will return.

We entered a landing pattern over a base surrounded by miles and miles of cement barriers and concertina wire. What happens to the barriers and wire after we leave? I wondered. They are eyesores that compact the soil and must damage wildlife habitats. American soldiers in machine-gun nests and up-armored Humvees with fifty calibers pulled perimeter guard. An immaculate palace in the center was protected by a wide moat and drawbridge, like something out of a fairy tale. I had been inside the Tikrit palace dozens of times, but the one in Baghdad was even grander.

The base had hundreds of trailers large enough to house two soldiers with hundreds of buildings left over from Saddam's army. During my two years in Iraq, I had come to believe that Saddam had put all of the country's resources into mosques, palaces, and the military. Does our country do the same with our resources? I wondered.

We landed and I ran with my head lowered outside of rotor distance as the blades continued to spin. The general saluted a few captains, majors and colonels then shook hands. I followed within a few feet, sitting right behind the general in a brand new pickup. The air conditioning blasted as the officers talked. I scanned. The first thing I noticed was that officers only had handguns and everybody else didn't even carry a weapon.

We parked by the palace and walked over a drawbridge where huge carp stared up at me waiting to be fed. How old are you guys? I wondered. Did you eat pieces of humans like I read about? We passed through huge doors to a cool marble galley with a chandelier worth more than all of the towns we passed. The general entered a secure room and his driver approached.

"Go grab a bite and be back by two," he said. "Take off your gear and leave your rifle here." He smiled and patted my shoulder. "And don't look so damn serious."

I set down my helmet and vest, kept two magazines in my back pockets, and a baseball cap in my hand before meandering around the palace in admiration. It was cool despite the 130-degree temperature outside. Bright colors and jewels adorn the floors, walls, and ceiling. I could swear the balustrade was gold. Was the entire place hand-painted? I wondered. I laughed at the irony, Saddam, the classy eccentric, was found living in a hole before he was hung. Vanity does not pay off.

American soldiers scurried around with pressed uniforms and spit-shined boots. Everybody had clean shiny hair that was combed. Plastic fold-out tables were covered in computers and wires ran everywhere. They looked busy and stressed, overweight or gym buff and clean. Nestle water bottles and candy wrappers were everywhere.

I walked outside into a heatwave and stopped on the drawbridge to watch the fish.

"They love MREs," said a gorgeous sergeant with clean skin and dark hair. She cut open a number 7 MRE and poured a pack of Beef Stew into the water. "I come here every day to feed them," she said. "Here—you want to try."

I shook my head. I couldn't believe she was pouring the best MRE in the water to feed fucking carp while infantrymen and locals were hungry.

"It brings me a lot of peace," she said. I tried not to look at her because I was so lonely and felt like a savage. "I may not be able to help the Iraqi people as I hoped, but at least I can feed their fish."

She laughed. I nodded and shrugged. I had to turn my head away from her because I could smell her shampoo and soap.

"Did you know that this type of fish can live to be hundreds of years old?" she said.

I shrugged. "These same fish were fed human flesh by Saddam and his brothers. Isn't that crazy?"

"There's a lot of crazy shit going on here," I said. "Do you know where the DFAC is, sergeant?" I asked. "I need some chow."

She pointed and gave me directions and I walked away. I saluted a dozen officers with fat cheeks, paunches, and to-go plates stacked on top of each other. Their cargo pockets swung with soda cans and Red Bull. I opened the door of the dining facility and stood in awe at the large number of soldiers and countless ethnic options of cuisine. "Shut the door!" Somebody yelled. "Don't let the flies in!" People laughed. I thought about my first tour, when we slept on the ground at the water treatment facility only a few feet from the latrine, flies covered us day and night.

I nodded, removed my hat to tuck in my cargo pocket, and found a seat in the back corner to watch both entrances.

My hair was twice as long as everybody's and my sideburns were way past regulation. I was stop-lossed, so I didn't give a shit. Soldiers laughed and talked like they were hanging out at a restaurant/bar back home, nobody seemed serious. Their rifles were all checked in at the armory and they did not seem worried or afraid.

I set my hat on the table to reserve my seat and slung my rifle. Holding it in both hands, I made sure the upside-down magazines were in my back pocket and ready to be loaded. The dining facility would be a perfect target for *hajji*. I went to where the food was served, the options were endless. Thai, Mexican, Caribbean, Vietnamese, Indian, American, Italian; a salad bar, a dessert bar with soft-serve ice cream, soda, juice, milk, water; everything besides middle eastern food. I shuffled between lines in a dream-like state settling on vegetarian green curry with salad. I had become a vegetarian after my divorce, desperately trying anything to make myself feel better. The vegetables were crisp and full of color, they seemed fresh. I grabbed a slice of refrigerated apple pie and covered it in soft serve vanilla ice cream then walked to the table with my tray. I was wearing my top with all of my badges, because in a world full of high-ranking pogues without badges mine earned me a lot of cred. They stared at me, I was proud to be a bad mother fucker surrounded by softies. I took the magazines out of my pockets and set them on the table. The sounds of laughter, chatter, and chewing drowned out the ringing in my ears.

The pretty sergeant entered and dozens of men turned their heads. I dropped mine, lifting it to peek at her as she moved gracefully to the Thai food line to talk and laugh with the cook. With her tray in her hands, she looked around and I dropped my head again.

"Mind if I sit here?" she said, directly across from me.

She had perfectly straight teeth and bright eyes, a slight southern accent, and a voice that was neither too high nor too low. She was stunning. I shrugged, and she sat down.

"You don't say much, do ya?" she said. I shrugged. It was the closest I had been to a woman in fifteen, eighteen, twenty-one months and my mind was racing. "It's a relief," she said. "The guys around here won't stop talking." She bowed her head to pray, made the sign of the cross then took a small bite. I peeked at her and noticed her clean neck free of dirt. "You have a lot of badges for a specialist."

"They make me wear them when I'm pulling security for the general," I said.

"Combat infantryman's badge, pathfinder, air assault, and a mustard stain on your jump wings that shows you parachuted into combat," she said. "When did you jump in?"

I shrugged. "March 26, 2003," I said. "As part of the northern front."

She used chopsticks to play with her pad thai before taking another tiny bite. She was so dang cute I couldn't look.

"You must be very brave," she said, and I blushed feeling tightness in my chest. "I have not done a single brave thing since I arrived," she said. "Unless you count eating the hamburgers they serve here. Who knows where the meat comes from?" She laughed as I hid a smile with my hand.

"You infantrymen are another breed, though. My daddy was infantry in 'Nam. He is a preacher now, though, back home in Baton Rouge. He doesn't talk about the war or the army, he never does. Where is your home?"

"Alaska," I said. "Seward, Alaska."

"So you are a real mountain man, huh?" she said. I shrugged and felt heat in my face and chest. "What do you think about the war?"

"I try not to," I said. "What's the point?"

She laughed, "That's all we do around here is talk about the war and how chaotic, pointless, and funny it is. Most of us haven't even left base, so we don't know what's happening out there outside of numbers and reports. To be honest, the only Iraqi I have seen is the man who cleans the Pizza Hut, and he is a very sweet man. You, on the other hand, a young specialist full of badges, I can see in your eyes that you know first hand about the horrors of this war, about the chaos, and you probably don't think it is funny at all."

I shrugged. "No more than the next guy."

"Why won't you look at me?" She said, leaning forward and trying to lock eyes. "Stop acting bashful."

"I don't act," I said. "And I'm not brave. I'm just doing what I have to to survive and get home."

She blushed, took a tiny bite, and said, "Well—I think you're brave. And I thank you for what you are doing."

I almost started tearing up. So I stood, put the magazines in my back pocket, and tapped them three times for good luck, then brought the tray to the dishwasher, an African from Sierra Leone being paid two dollars and fifty cents an hour. I locked eyes with the pretty sergeant one last time, waved, and walked outside.

"Stay alert, stay alive," I said to myself. "Don't get wrapped up in emotions."

I sat and watched the carp for thirty minutes or so while thinking about the eternal spirit that Railroad Joe had told me about, before going inside to put on my helmet and vest. In the helicopter, the general picked the hell hole again to my dismay and we flew to a small infantry outpost where thin young men with sunken eyes played cards, smoked, and dipped. They stared at me like I was a spy. I was clean and healthy compared to them. I wanted to tell them about my first tour but knew it didn't matter. They lived under ponchos that were buttoned together and tied with 550 cord to tent poles. They blew in the wind and made a lot of noise. They slept on cots with a box of possessions tucked under and a ruck at their heads. Their rifles were within arms reach. Women did not exist outside of magazines, letters, and memory. The camp was silent besides the wind whipping the ponchos and an occasional burst of laughter. Smoke from a burning barrel of shit and piss mixed with sand and blew all around.

We left after an hour and the general took the hell hole again. We flew over the salt flats to a memorial service for a woman who was killed by a stray mortar two days before leaving the country. Her boots, rifle, helmet, and dog tags were set up traditionally as bagpipes played taps. Her platoon sergeant fought back tears while describing her as a fun-loving Christian who always raised morale.

"She believed in this mission," he said, between sniffles. "She wanted to save these people."

Dozens of soldiers wiped their faces. I glanced at the general's straight face and dark sunglasses just as he wiped a tear with a glove. I cried too.

We left before dark. The general was in the hell hole again, immobile except for his cheeks blowing in the wind. We flew low over power lines next to the highway with the long row of wavy cars, and the soldiers in *hajji* wraps waved. The general did not wave back, I did.

When I returned to the safe house, my team leader approached me in Scooby-Doo pajamas.

"How'd the mission go?" He asked.

I shrugged.

"The massage lady is open for another hour," he said. "Get over there, it's on me." He handed me a twenty that I stuffed in my pocket before he carried his laptop into the clean latrine.

I t was springtime in Iraq, yet I had not seen a single flower. I did not see any flowers, plants, butterflies, birds, or bees between March 2003 to February 2004, or November 2005 to November 2006, none that I can remember at least. Iraq is a beautiful country, nonetheless. Private Freeborn drew a flower on his kevlar cover and wrote, "Warflower" underneath. He was called a faggot and teased until forced to replace the cover with a new one. I secretly loved the flower, I think we all did. I did not realize how much I appreciated flowers until being without them, such is the case with many things, I have come to learn. Sometimes I felt like a microscopic petal on a wilting daisy plucked at by God, chance, karma. "Let him live, let him die. Let him live, let him die." A twisted interstellar game. Of course, I did not think of this metaphor while in Iraq, and it is the best I can come up with fifteen years later from my safe homestead on twenty acres in Happy Valley, Alaska. Where

I fluctuate between periods of extreme isolation and guilt, contentment and acceptance.

Freeborn pulled back the concertina wire to let our Humvees pass.

"Kill them mother fuckers," he said, a fresh kevlar cover glowing in the dark.

We locked and loaded, prepared to do just that.

It was too dark to see without night vision goggles. Everything was black and green and when I tilted my head back I saw only shadows. We were living at an abandoned school, where two weeks prior I went room to room with my rifle in the pocket of my shoulder hoping not to find a classroom full of kids. There were no desks, papers, or people, nothing but dead air; it was like something from Resident Evil, I expected rabid dogs.

Nobody spoke, we hardly did anymore. Not Brammer, Sully, Alvarez, or I. Because all we thought about anymore was sex, affection, food, and going home, and we always felt worse when we talked about them. So we acted like they didn't exist—like nothing existed besides what was directly in front of us, and we didn't even know if that was real. We were living Buddhas with heavy weapons and soul scars. We oriented our bodies outward to scan roadsides, fields, roofs, and doorways. The sound of Humvee engines was hypnotic.

Trench warfare, jungle rot, punji stakes, Nazis, carpet bombs, and visible bad guys did not exist in my war; desperation, loneliness, fear, and hopelessness did. What would my friends and family say if I returned? Where would I fit in?

I wanted to tell my mother that human beings were trying to kill us because we invaded their country and that I would do the same thing if people invaded my country and I was brave enough. I wanted to tell her that every second I was awake I thought about killing just so I would not be killed. The worst part was that I did not know whom to kill, and I did not want anybody to be killed, but since we were there, killing was inevitable. I wanted to tell her that they were hitting us hard with improvised explosive devices, small arms fire, and rocket-propelled grenades, and then maybe she would think I was brave. Maybe she would sense fear in my voice. I wanted to tell her the story of when I fell backward into a trench of human shit after the LT's vehicle was hit and the RTO was on his knees in the road and Milton stumbled around the center of the road covered in blood as *hajji* fired from the hillside. I wanted to tell her that I hate hills but love mountains because I haven't had anybody try to kill me in the mountains. I wanted her to hold me like she did when I was a little boy and tell me that she would be worried if I did not cry and that she loved me before, during, and after the war. I wanted to describe the dazzling light show as fifty calibers and mark 19s destroyed the hillside. How the most beautiful thing I had seen since the last firefight was the new one. I wanted her to think that I was brave. I wanted her to hold me like she did when I was an innocent boy as I explained what it meant to be a member of the dismount squad. How we climbed over the tailgate at every stop to pull security, search houses, sweep fields, and clear buildings. How we fired from our knees, bellies, and boots. I wanted to tell her that I was tired of climbing over tailgates and that all I wanted was to ride in a car with the windows down next to a body of saltwater listening to Cat Power or Bob Seger.

The stories would contain chaos, followed by stillness, followed by chaos, without any linear movement. How else could I tell them? Would I ever tell them?

Brammer, Alvarez, and I dismounted to clear a field while the village on the hill burned. I was terrified somebody would pop up and shoot. I would skip that part of the story, though, nobody needs to know that infantrymen have fear. I would say, "It was pitch black without a moon, and clouds covered the sky. I jumped over a narrow trench and lost my balance on the other side, slipping and falling backward into a stagnant stream of human shit. I panicked and flopped around like Loveall on the drop zone until Alvarez grabbed my forearm and yanked me out." Mother would laugh when I told her, I know she would and she would say something clever like: "Holy shit!" and I would continue telling her stories for hours that passed like seconds.

I wanted to explain the fear I carried like a dead weight in my rucksack from never knowing who was good or bad. The fear didn't stop when I returned home when I started believing that everybody was a bad guy, including myself. But I could not tell her any stories, I did not tell her any stories before she died, because I am supposed to act like everything is okay all the time, but the truth is, everything is not okay.

If my mother would have asked, "Didn't you feel bad for scaring so many people?"

I would have shrugged, laughed, and lied.

"I don't feel bad about anything anymore." I would have said, then stretched my arms like a flower reaching for the sun.

PART II

My first sunrise as a free man wasn't as marvelous as I had expected, nothing is. I was twenty-two years old, divorced, and disappointed. After spending two weeks obtaining signatures from every hidden building on Fort Campbell, and turning in my used equipment, I signed the honorable discharge papers and left base. It was a breeze to enlist, a storm to get out. I drove north to Hopkinsville to car camp in the parking lot of an office building where I would have a final medical exam the next morning.

A vehicle entered and I watched the driver; I had returned from my second tour two weeks prior and was still reaching for my rifle. I flipped open the phone to check the time.

6:30 a.m. —zero calls, zero texts.

I searched through my contacts for someone to share my newfound joy, hesitating at Elliot's name. I regretted not picking her forget-me-not flowers before the war, perhaps things would be different now. I turned off the phone to be alone by choice.

With an hour and a half until the appointment, I stepped from the Subaru station wagon into crisp, cool Kentucky air. It was September 19, 2006. Rusty needles covered gangly pines with pointy orange tips like tracer rounds. I knelt for cover behind the car to brush my teeth with water from a five-gallon jug, lit a smoke, and walked. I stood on a grassy knoll watching workers arrive as they watched me. The smell of wet grass almost made me smile, but I didn't want to look crazy so I didn't. I had sure missed the smell of wet grass.

I thought, The infantry motto is "Follow Me," but I don't know whom to follow. Where will I go? What will I do? Who cares?

I had sixty-thousand dollars in the bank, nobody to share it with, and no idea what to do.

"Everything is still dark after my discharge," I whispered to a solitary ant on my finger. "I thought the hard times were over." I set it down and watched it scurry away. Thin pink clouds floated across the sky like jellyfish, I needed to go to the ocean. I inhaled smoke deep into my lungs and held it until I couldn't stand it then exhaled and watched it rise and disappear. "If only memories vanished like smoke." I spun the cigarette in my fingertips while staring at the ember, recalling when the guys from the third platoon stacked those bodies for photographs. I didn't take a picture, but I watched, just like I watched them piss on them and laugh. Why didn't I say anything? I wondered. More vehicles and workers arrived with staring judgmental eyes so I went to the car to check the time. Five minutes to eight, almost time.

I wasn't surprised nobody had called or texted to congratulate me, who would? I distanced myself from everybody when I left home, even more so after my first tour. They just didn't understand.

I had made my first resume during out-processing and quickly realized that being an infantryman does not transfer well. Battle Drill 1 Alpha did not matter anymore; neither did being able to shoot a moving target at three hundred meters, or clear a series of houses while moving through a hostile environment. They would not land me a job as a teacher, and I sure as shit didn't want to pull security or do private contract work or do any job that required I carry a weapon. And I had far too much pride to be a custodian. The more I thought about it the more I realized that I didn't want a job at all, but I sure as hell couldn't go to college and be around silver-spooned kids with well-articulated opinions. I would go fucking postal. Maybe I would travel to Latin America and learn Spanish; find a cheap bungalow on the beach to write, surf, and cuddle with a beautiful woman. I could drink beer and smoke weed all day until I passed out.

I left my thoughts behind to enter an office building and jog up two flights of concrete stairs to where a silver-haired woman was seated behind a desk wearing huge turquoise earrings.

"Good morning," she greeted, with a big smile and radiant cheer.

"Morning, ma'am," I said.

"And how are you on this fine morning?"

"Good," I said. "And you?"

She leaned forward to rest her heavy chest on the keyboard and looked both ways. I wondered what word her breasts had typed.

"I didn't sleep a wink last night," she said, with a quiet southern accent. "My husband of thirty-three years snores like a freight train, even the cat can't sleep." I hid a smile with my hand as she laughed. "He has a disorder that stops his breathing, and I swear to God sometimes I wish he'd just pack his bag and leave. It causes me more trouble than him, I know that."

"One day, he'll stop breathing," I said. "We all do."

"You're right about that," she said. "I don't know how I made it this many years." She coughed into a paper towel. "Pardon me." She patted her chest and glanced both ways with a red face. "Actually," she whispered. "Between you and me, I sleep three nights a week in our son's room just to catch up."

"Is that right?" I said, shifting my weight nervously. "You're lucky to have that room."

"You're right about that," she said, pausing for a response. "So how can I help you this morning, young man?"

"Today is my first day as a free man," I said. "And I'm here for an exam."

"We wouldn't live in such a great country if not for young men like you," she said. I didn't know if she was mocking me or being serious, so I kept my lips peeled. "What are you going to do with your life now?"

I took a deep breath and said: "Drive across the country to try and fall in love with America. Then go home to Alaska."

"That's what all you boys need to do," she said. "After all that you've done for our country, you deserve to take a little break. You have quite a long drive ahead of you, so let's get you in to see the doctor so you can get on the road." She engulfed the mouse with her big hand and then typed. "The weather reports say that if you wait much longer you'll run into snowfall."

"It's that time of year," I said.

"Be safe, now," she said. "I'm sure people are waiting." I shrugged. "I see you're down for eight o'clock, and that makes you our first appointment of the morning." She raised her hands in celebration.

"Does that come with a prize or something?"

"Hmm," she opened and closed the drawers. "Let's see… How about a pen?" She held up a fine point black pen. "You never know when you'll need to write something down. And you know the old saying, 'The pen is mightier than the sword.'"

I thanked her and put the pen behind my ear.

"Thank you again for what you did for our country," she said. I turned away, wondering if the Iraqis would thank me. "Have a seat and the doctor will be with you in a minute."

I sat in the back corner to watch the entrance and found an old National Geographic with a cover story on Kurdistan. I flipped through the pages and found an article with pictures of Kurds in the same mountains where I was, pictures of mass graves from Saddam's executions, and pictures of crying, heavy-set women. I closed the magazine and tucked it under a smiling white woman on Women's Weekly.

Maybe some of the Iraqis are thankful, I thought, just as the doctor opened the door.

"You must be Robert," she said.

"Yes, ma'am," I stood and walked towards her.

"Come with me, please, and we will get the exam underway." I followed her. "This is where we will conduct your hearing test." She pointed at a soundproof room on the left. "But first, let's do some paperwork." I sat down across from her at her desk. "Did you use earplugs while firing your rifle?"

I laughed, it was not the norm and often the last thing on my mind. She nodded. Even though she was twenty or thirty years older than me, she was the most beautiful woman I had been within arms reach of in over a year. After the questions, I entered the testing room, closed the door, and sat on a stool watching her through the glass. I removed the headphones from a hook on the wall and placed them over my ears.

"Can you hear me?" I gave her two thumbs up. "Okay, raise your right hand when you hear a sound in your right ear and left hand when you hear a sound in your left ear, and raise both hands when you hear sounds in both ears." I nodded and gave her two thumbs up. "Are there any questions?" I shook my head. "Then, let's begin."

I closed my eyes to focus. In the beginning, beeps were loud and I raised my hands with confidence, then they became dim and questionable and I raised them with a 'why not' attitude until finally, I raised them only because they had been down too long.

"Okay, Mr. Stark," she said. "That's it; please hang up the headphones and come out so we can get you on the road."

"Is that it?" I asked, standing by her desk. "Am I really finished?"

"That's it," she said, writing notes on a clipboard. I started pacing. "I will record your results and send them to the VA to see if you qualify for disability."

"But no, really," I said, with a shaky voice. "Is there anything else? There must be more."

She stopped writing, removed her glasses, and looked at me with sympathetic eyes.

"You can go home now," she said. "I am sure people are waiting."

I nodded and continued pacing. "How does the VA decide whether I qualify or not," I asked, "and when will I find out?"

"When you first joined the army, you were administered the same standardized hearing test. The VA will compare the tests to see if your hearing worsened. It can take anywhere from two weeks to a year to process a claim, and because of the large number of claims from soldiers returning from Iraq and Afghanistan, it is hard to say how long it will take."

I rocked back and forth. "I've been dreaming about this day for a long time. It's just, that it's hard to believe it's finally here. And I don't know what to do now that I can do anything."

She smiled and nodded. "I suggest you go downstairs, start your car, and start driving. I am sure people are waiting."

I pictured my mother on the phone in Arizona, where she had moved after her husband was transferred; my brother was currently living and working in Juneau, and Elliot was probably suntanning naked beside her boyfriend on a beach in Orange County.

"Maybe you're right," I said, walking to the door. "Thanks a lot. I hope you have a good life."

"Always remember," she said, "to love yourself first."

I laughed and left.

"Thanks for the pen," I told the lady at the desk.

"Remember what I said. 'The pen is mightier than the sword.'"

I sprinted down the concrete stairs and flew out the door into a world that was much brighter than when I entered. I ran and skipped to the car like a little boy yelping with excitement, opened the door, and shouted at the top of my lungs "I am free! I am free! Thank God I am free!" An elderly couple stepped out of a Lincoln Continental and looked at me like a crazy person. I apologized, removed the pen from my ear to place in the glove box, and lit a cigarette.

"Here we go."

I turned the ignition and the old Subaru wagon purred as Bob Dylan's "Masters of War" blasted on the speakers. I whipped it in reverse and almost peeled out of the parking lot. It was all just a bad dream that I was finally waking up from. The further I traveled from Fort Campbell, the better off I would be.

I passed through Nashville without stopping, accelerating from sixty to seventy until the car shook like a body during muscle failure. So I slowed down to cruise past Nashville toward Memphis while chain-smoking Turkish Jades. Hours later, as I passed the glass pyramid in Memphis, I reflected on the time Sergeant Milton and the RTO were covered in blood stumbling around the middle of the road after an IED blast hit their truck. I could hear the Mark-19 launch grenades and destroy a series of mud huts on the hill. Whose homes were they? Who was inside? I drove on chain-smoking, telling myself to forget about it, reminding myself that I was just a kid who did what he had to do to survive; I was not a puppet for the American regime. I had tried to be kind; like making sure sandbags were loose enough over detainees' heads so they could breathe, and zip ties were loose enough that their wrists didn't swell too bad, and when they shivered on the floor of the truck bed I covered them with my poncho liner even though they smelled bad. Hell, I only shot at people who shot at me.

I crossed over the Mississippi River into Arkansas as rays of red spread across the western sky; a gift for my survival. I pulled over to watch the sunset as the wind blew me west towards the Pacific. I decided to focus on the positive, like the fact that I was in Arkansas and not Iraq, reminding myself that the bad times are over and that it's time to focus on the good, only I couldn't conjure up anything good in my life other than having money in the bank. So I continued driving, I wouldn't stop until I was exhausted.

Mother moved to Coolidge, Arizona during my second tour where she rented a trailer in a gated community after transferring between Safeway stores. She had two friends, one was an eccentric Wiccan longtime friend who had married a man half her age doing life in prison for murdering his parents, and a seventy-six-year-old jack-of-all-trades named Paul. Paul was a secret the women kept from their jealous husbands. The women worked together and lived together in a one-bedroom trailer, and when they were off work they either visited their husbands or sunbathed in the front yard while talking to their husbands on the phone. Over the years I have concluded that prison marriages are very similar to military marriages, both parties live secret lives and only reveal what they want the other person to know.

Mother worked forty to sixty hours a week, rushed home to answer the phone, and talked through supper and movies until bedtime. She spent three and a half hours at the prison twice a day during her days off. She had recently declared bankruptcy due to long-distance calls after her husband was transferred before she had moved, which is why she, and many other prison spouses, move from town to town and stay below the poverty line. Mother knew firsthand that prisons are big businesses that rob the poor, and that colored people are punished much more severely than whites. Mother was often singled out and banned from visiting not because she had broken any rules, but because she was a white woman married to a black man. The white prison guards didn't approve. Either way, my mother had been married to Victor for eight years at that point, the happiest years of her life.

I reached for a cigarette in an empty pack and then pulled into the next gas station. A bell announced my entrance and a cute brunette with straight hair and hazel eyes smiled behind the counter. I wanted to touch her and be touched by her, but I could barely even look at her.

"Hello," I said, lifting the bill of my cap.

She turned around to restock cigarettes as I approached the counter while admiring her tight jeans, strong legs, and pumpkin butt. She wore a green and black checkered flannel over tight black jeans and she smelled like menthols.

"What can I get ya'?"

She had pale skin and freckles, I love freckles. I almost forgot to speak, until she put her hand on her hip and shifted her weight from leg to leg.

"Two packs of Lucky Strikes, please," I said, nervously.

"Is that all?" She bit her lower lip and I noticed how white her teeth and irises were.

"Yes, ma'am, that's all."

She turned around and bent over without bending a knee, searching the bottom row with delicate hands and long clean fingers. I tried to be a gentleman but could not resist the urge to stare at her perfect butt.

"Where are the Lucky Strikes," she asked, "do you see 'em?" Although I did see them, I couldn't seem to talk. She stood on her tippy toes and reached high tightening her ass and flexing her hamstrings. I could see dimples in her lower back. She turned to face me, shrugged her shoulders, and licked her lips. "Is there anything else you'd like?" she said. "I can't find 'em." She lifted the side of her shirt to scratch a fresh owl tattoo. The doorbell rang and a three chinned man with camouflage hunting clothes ruined my opportunity to ask her out.

"The Lucky Strikes are on top," I said. "Right behind you."

She found them as if she had known all along. I paid and said goodbye as she probably rolled her eyes. I packed the smokes, filled the tank, and lit the third cigarette from the right while driving away rubbing the stubble on my chin.

"It's about time I grew my first beard," I said. "If anybody asks what I'm doing with my life, I'll tell them that I'm growing a beard." I laughed and pounded the steering wheel. It felt good to laugh. I stopped at a 24-hour diner to eat a shit ton of calories before continuing west until I couldn't physically drive, then I parked at a rest stop to chain smoke with the window cracked until passing out. Life was all right.

20

7:45 a.m. —zero calls, zero texts. I skipped brushing my teeth to smoke instead and without thinking, I called Elliot. The ringing was magnified as I waited for her voice on the other end. There was no answer. I hung up the phone and turned it off to be alone by choice. Focus on the good, focus on the good, I told myself. There wasn't a cloud in the sky yet everything seemed foggy; hell, I was free to rush from state to state without anybody bothering me or slowing me down.

I tried to make eye contact with other drivers as they flew past, but they were either staring ahead, talking and laughing with fellow passengers, or talking and laughing on cell phones.

"Do you see your fellow American?" I asked. "Traveling this open road just like you. Look at me, Goddammit, look at me! Let me know that I exist…" But they paid me no mind like I was just another homeless veteran without a house holding a cardboard sign. Ignored uncomfortably before being later discussed.

I had decided months prior while still in Iraq that when the time came to drive home, I would stop anytime I felt like it, no matter how insignificant. I wanted to camp under the stars and experience new parts of the foreign land we Alaskans call "The Lower Forty-Eight." I wanted to build campfires to roast potatoes in tin foil and eat baked beans while reading Robert Service and Gary Snyder. I wanted to clean my only spoon in a creek and dry it on my pants. I wanted to explore the deserts of my own country and replace bad memories with good. At least that was the idea before I began closing the gap between mother and me; the Pacific Ocean and me; Alaska and me; Home and me.

After driving through and destroying farmers' crops in Iraq, I wanted a piece of property to farm, live simply, and be a steward of the Earth. To escape much of the chaos and confusion of the world. To grow enough food to supplement with salmon for much of my family's food, and to sell the excess. I certainly did not want to be around people because I did not want to talk about what I did in Iraq or what my country does to other countries or minorities within our own country, nor did I want to brainstorm ideas about what to do differently. I wanted to focus on the Earth as a way to escape America. But since I promised Mother a road trip, I would stick to my word and visit Arizona first.

I pulled into a rest area after a long day of driving without seeing anything but the road to chain smoke and think among idling trucks.

When I returned to Italy after my first tour, I was on high alert. Boogeymen with turbans and guns hid in shadows ready to detonate. Complacency kills. I woke up covered in sweat searching for my grenade launcher. I looked behind me while walking to ensure rear security. I scanned roofs, ditches, doorways, vehicles, potholes, boxes, and people. Everybody and everything was a threat. The only way I could relax was by drinking to the point of passing out. It wasn't good.

My mother once advised, "If you're going to join the military, make it the air force, they know how to take care of their soldiers." And I wished I would have listened.

When my platoon was put on restriction after the Highway to Hell incident, we were sent to Camp Renegade in Kirkuk to redeploy back to Italy; I couldn't believe how populated the camp had become since we moved in 11 months prior. I quickly noticed the advantages of being in the Air Force. They had a swimming pool where pretty girls wore bikinis and buff men did backflips. Everybody laughed. They did three-month deployments with pretty women and had relaxed standards on haircuts and relaxed leaders. They served delicious food and had a USO building with thousands of free books, air conditioning, phones to call home, and places for people to hang out and watch movies. Did I mention they had pretty women everywhere?

On the first day at camp, we were in line at the army dining facility when a sergeant first class with a pressed uniform and no badges started yelling at Milton and UFC for allowing their squad to be such sorry excuses for soldiers. Our hair was long, and our uniforms were filthy. We hadn't had time to shave and we were exhausted. The asshole sergeant made UFC and Milton stand at parade rest in front of dozens of soldiers while he yelled at them for their bad leadership and threatened to report them to higher-ups. Milton told Brammer, Sully, Alvarez, and I to go in and grab some chow even though all we wanted to do was tell the guy that he was a fucking idiot. We listened to our leader. Inside the chow hall, we watched a fat soldier sit his tray of food down to grab a slice of cheesecake, and when he returned to the table he noticed a fly on the food and disgustingly picked up the tray and dumped all of the food in the garbage before filling another plate, only after eating his cheesecake. I was pissed. Both of the men were lifers, no doubt, who had sat on their butts for months on a safe base and will later go home and wear the hats and earn the awards.

That night we took showers, and I could hardly recognize the skinny, sunken-faced, cold-eyed man in the mirror.

The following day, I recognized a girl pulling guard outside of the air force chow hall and she stared at me as if she knew me. I approached her after lunch and realized it was a girl from Seward. So we talked about home and decided to meet up after her shift when she lent me a DVD series about Superman and we took a walk. She complained about her deployment, about the heat of pulling guard for three hours outside of the chow hall and not getting enough sleep; about her fear of mortars, after being attacked twice with the explosions close enough to feel them. She said it was scary and I nodded. It was wild to be around someone from back home, I didn't know if I should be the goofy high school teen or the deadpan war teen.

The confusing part about Mother's advice was that her father was an air force security officer who trained German shepherds. He did two tours in Vietnam. He left home as a loving, affectionate father, husband, and neighbor. He was the type of guy everybody wanted to be around. But when he returned from Vietnam, he built a shed in the backyard to live alone and drink himself to death. When his kids would climb on his lap, he would bawl because they reminded him of the murdered kids in Vietnam. He died at 43 from cirrhosis of the liver. I never had the chance to meet him.

Memories and guilt got the best of him, I thought. Would they do the same to me?

I opened my eyes, surprised to have fallen asleep. I was thankful to be alive and to have a dry, bug-free bed. I stepped out of the car under a starry sky, recognizing the north star and big dipper. With palms together, I thanked the Cosmos and whispered: "I'm coming home."

I used the latrine to brush my teeth and wash my face, smiling at my growing beard. I was hungry for something more than food, but I didn't know what, so I found a diner named Jimmy P's to eat breakfast.

I walked through a swinging glass door where two women with gray hair glanced at me from behind the bar. One was tall and built, the other was short and fat, like Arnold and Danny Devito in *Twins*.

"Take a seat anywhere you'd like, darling," said the tall one.

I sat at a booth beside the window to stare at the half-crescent moon and rising sun. The short waitress grabbed a pot of coffee, a pitcher of water, and a menu.

"Would you like some coffee, dear?" she filled my glass.

"Yes, ma'am," I said.

She filled the grey mug an inch below the brim.

"Cream and sugar?"

"No, thank you."

She filled it the rest of the way.

"How you doin' this mornin', hon?" she said.

"Fine, thank you. Yourself?"

"Like my daddy always said, rest his soul, 'Same thing a different day, keeps a restless heart at bay.' I've been doing this job for thirteen years without a sick day."

"That's impressive."

"I wouldn't say all that now," she said. "It ain't rocket science..." she paused for a moment then continued. "I'll give you a minute, hon, call me over when you're ready."

She went behind the counter to talk with the other lady.

On the cover of the menu was a picture of a man with a big beard holding three Rottweilers on thick chains with one hand. He showed no sign of struggle while the dogs yanked their chains tight.

I raised my hand when I was ready.

"What are you having, hon?"

"A three-egg breakfast with hash browns and toast," I said.

"How would you like your eggs?"

"Scrambled, please, with some cheddar cheese."

"White or wheat?"

"Wheat, please, and a glass of orange juice."

"Bacon or sausage?"

"Can I replace the bacon with pancakes?" I said. "I'll pay the difference."

"Of course, you can," she said, writing on a pad. "You're the one paying. Let me put that order in for ya then I'll get your drinks filled."

She walked through swinging doors into the kitchen and returned a minute later with a cup of orange juice and refills. She returned to leaning on the counter just as the man in the picture came out of the kitchen holding a ticket and whispered something to the waitress. He waved at me when our eyes met, I assumed he was Jimmy P.

Please don't ask about my vegetarianism, I thought.

As he went in back, I noticed a woman drinking coffee at the end of the bar while doing a crossword. The bell rang and the tall waitress grabbed a plate of french toast smothered in butter and set it in front of the girl with a bottle of syrup. The girl inhaled the steam.

"Mmm…" she said. "Thank you, Dolores. This looks ravishing."

"No problem, June," she said. "Go on and enjoy your breakfast now, before it turns cold." She refilled her coffee before doing the same for me.

I almost forgot what it was like to be cared for by a woman or to be in the company of women. The ladies leaned against the counter drinking coffee watching the sunrise. The girl at the counter removed a beanie to reveal short, bleach blonde hair with a devil's lock. She tucked it behind her ear to eat. Suddenly, I had an urge to pour syrup over her naked body and lick it off. I felt like a wild animal. I turned to look outside to distract myself, but then noticed a handful of bracelets on her wrist and a light blue shirt barely covering her back. She had on a tan belt with amber stones that held up her tight, black jeans.

My sex life is pathetic, I thought. I'm twenty-two years old and I haven't been with a woman in almost two years. Hell, at any moment I could be pushing up daisies.

The waitress refilled my mug and my mind stopped drifting. I held the warm mug to steady my nerves and be present.

Elliot had sent me dozens of postcards from Thailand, Nepal, Egypt, and Costa Rica; packages with pictures, letters, taffy, and tobacco; she made a birthday card that was signed by all the homies I thought had forgotten me. She wrote things like: "What you are doing is important," and "You are making the world safer," even if she didn't believe it.

I wished the girl eating french toast was Elliot. I was disappointed when she looked back and smiled; like I always am when a woman with a similar style to Elliot is not Elliot. The bell rang and two plates of food were set in the window and the short waitress carried them over.

"Here you go, hon'," she said. "I'll get you more coffee."

"Thank you, ma'am," I said. "This looks amazing."

"You goin' to need anything else now?"

Hot sauce, syrup, jam, salt, and pepper were on the table.

"I'm set, thank you."

She refilled my mug and then returned to leaning on

the counter talking about things I probably would not understand. I inhaled deeply and smiled.

"Thank you," I whispered. "Give me strength to make it through the day, amen."

I closed my eyes for the first bite of pancakes, savoring the sweet and salty combination. I covered the eggs and hash browns with hot sauce and spread a thick layer of butter on the toast. I envied the waitresses, who seemed content leaning against a counter staring out a window. They had a purpose while I had none.

What brought them here? I wondered. Is Jimmy P. married to one?

The sexy girl leaned forward and pulled a wallet out of her back pocket. She paid, said goodbye, and walked out while I stared at her pumpkin ass like a creep. I poured more syrup on the pancakes and ketchup on the hash browns.

It was respectful of the waitress not to ask why I replaced meat with pancakes, I thought. People worry too much about things that aren't their business, I'm one of them.

"You going to be wantin' anything else, hon?" she said. "A piece of homemade pie?"

"I'm stuffed, thanks."

"Whenever you feel like payin' come on up to the counter," she said. "Take as long as you need.'" She grabbed the plates and walked into the kitchen.

Maybe someday I'll have a purpose, I thought.

I watched the sun expose herself fully over the horizon, paid the tab, and left a ten-dollar tip.

22

I planned to stay at my buddy Elroy Longhorn's place in Fort Smith that night after he had promised me some cold beer, a hot, and a cot. I called him after passing Little Rock, Arkansas and he said I still had a few hours and to give him a ring after Clarksville.

"Clarksville?" I said. "I just left Clarksville."

"There is no escape, Stark," he said laughing. "No matter how far you run, your past is always there."

Elroy Longhorn is forty-seven years old and has been in the active-duty Army for over half his life. He was the coolest, most laid-back old-timer in my Pathfinder unit. He often talked about retiring and riding a Harley across the country with his wife in the sidecar and a big bag of weed in the saddlebag. He claimed to have a refrigerator in his garage full of beer as the only way to get friends over yet he hadn't drank in sixteen years. Not since he wrecked a motorcycle and almost died. I didn't believe anybody who said they didn't drink.

I stayed in the slow lane through Conway into Russelville watching cars pass. I was heading in the right direction, west—towards home. I patted the dash and lit a smoke. I called Elroy, who said I was forty-five minutes out, so I stepped on the gas until the car shook. The sun was down by the time I pulled into Ft. Smith, which was right on the border with Oklahoma. I had pictured a military town full of strip malls, car dealerships, and bars, but it wasn't like that, at least not what I saw. It had Mom and Pop stores with names I had never heard of; restaurants, hardware stores, and grocery stores with unfamiliar signs. Neighborhoods were lined with old leafy trees with leaves falling on quiet streets. I imagined there were still small-town problems. Parents pushing children too hard in sports and academics, and those not pushing enough; everybody knows everybody's sex life, even if they are fabrications; boredom; too high rates on garbage pickup, electricity, and plumbing; teen pregnancy; abortion; damnation; drugs and alcohol; hell, at least there aren't bombs dropping and children covered in burns from unexploded ordinances.

"Almost there," I said, patting the dashboard. Think positive, be positive.

I followed Elroy's directions through gorgeous, dark, and quiet neighborhoods with wide, leafy streets until parking in front of his house, packing the night's essentials in a backpack, and walking up brick stairs. Just as I was about to knock, Elroy swung open the door.

"If it isn't Bob Stark," he said. "I didn't think I would

see the day you showed your face in good old Fort Smith, Arkansas."

"Thanks, Elroy," I said, patting my heart. "It's an honor."

He hugged me and invited me in, then rested his left hand on his belly and flicked his nose with his right hand. He was wearing board shorts and an "Old Guys Rule" tee-shirt. "Welcome to my home," he said, with wide-open arms. "How does it feel to be a free man?"

"I feel okay," I said. "I'll be better with a cold beer."

"Does it feel as great as you thought it would?"

"It's hard to realize that I'm free," I said. "I didn't think the day would come, and I'm not sure what to do."

"Just take your time," he said. "You'll find something fun and productive to stay occupied until you die. That's all we can do. I am glad you stuck it out, though. I was worried about you at the end. I thought maybe you would get kicked out."

"You're not the only one."

"All of that is behind you now," he said, patting my back. "Welcome to the great state of Arkansas and the lovely town of Fort Smith." He waved his arms. "Mi casa es su casa."

"Gracias, amigo." I removed my shoes and then set my pack down by a couch.

"The beer is in the refrigerator in the garage," he said. "Are you hungry?"

"A little bit," I said, "but I could go for a beer."

He led me to the garage and opened the fridge, and lo and behold it was full from top to bottom with craft beer.

"You gonna have one with me?" I asked.

"No, no, no… it's been 17 years now and I'm not about to start where I left off."

I opened one and drank it halfway down.

"I won't lie, Elroy," I said. "It's comforting to know I will not have to go back to Iraq."

"I'm sure it is," he said. "Unless they call you up for ready reserves."

"That won't happen," I said. "I'll go on the run."

We walked back inside to sit on bar stools in the kitchen.

"If you're hungry, eat," he said. "Don't be shy. We have enough food to keep a 3-man surveillance team in a hole for months."

I finished my first beer, went into the garage, and grabbed two more.

"I couldn't be sober," I said. "It would take the fun out of life."

I noticed a wood frame full of concert stubs on the wall with names like Pink Floyd, Grateful Dead, Led Zeppelin, Bob Dylan, Jimi Hendrix, The Doors, Janis Joplin, The Beatles, Bob Marley, David Bowie, Leonard Cohen, Creedence Clearwater Revival, The Band, George Jones, Johnny Cash and more. Plants were everywhere and huge windows faced south; brand new leather furniture with matching drapes, bookshelf, molding, and trim, all scarlet. Too perfect to sit or touch. A woman entered the kitchen with a cane.

"Hello," she held out her hand. "I am Elroy's wife, Karen, it is a pleasure to meet you."

"It's an honor, ma'am," I said. We shook. "I've heard a lot about you."

"And I you," she said.

"Thank you for opening your home."

"It is a pleasure to have guests," she said. "One cannot have enough. Did you see the concert tickets?"

"Yes, ma'am. Where did you get the ticket stubs?"

"Elroy kept them in his dresser for thirty years tucked under his underwear and socks," she said. "He didn't know what to do with them but refused to throw them away. Until the idea came to me in a dream." She sat on a stool to begin the tale. "Elroy was sleeping and snoring louder than a freight train. He is lovely when he sleeps." He blushed and they held hands. "I thought about the many nights I had missed him while he was away while watching his handsome, calm face. After I fell asleep, I was awakened by a swarm of bees buzzing in my face."

"'Bzzz bzzz bzzz,' they said. 'Bzzz bzzz bzzz.'" She motioned with her hand. "Elroy sat up, looked at me, and said: 'In the wood, they are best, together they rest.' He fell right back asleep and didn't remember it the next day."

"Still don't," said Elroy.

"A bee landed on the dresser and I knew what had to be done." Elroy stared at her like it was the first time he had heard the story. I chugged a beer. "A week later, I left the hospital with this cane and woke up in bed alone. Elroy was in Iraq, with you I suppose, and I had no way to contact him. So I set out to find a frame for the stubs, in hopes that he would stay home with me after he retired."

"Wow," I said. "It is a fine frame. So what about the bees? Were they real? Was it a dream? What do they mean?"

She smiled, "Sometimes it can be difficult to differentiate what is quote and quote 'real' and not," she said. "And it doesn't matter either, because it's real to you. You should have seen his eyes when he opened it."

Elroy wiped his eyes and went to the garage to grab me two beers. He cut lime into eight wedges and stuck a wedge in each beer.

"Congratulations, Bob," he said, handing me the beers. "To your freedom, adventure, and a long, happy life." I drank half a beer. "I am proud to see you leave with an honorable discharge. I promise it will pay off."

It was my first time drinking as a free man and nothing had changed, I could not stop.

"I know I promised you a joint of the finest Arkansas herb," he said, "but I can't find any, and neither can my wife." Karen shook her head and shrugged. "Our friends are dry, even our niece, Brenna Mae, doesn't have any."

"It's all right, Elroy," I said. "I'll be fine."

"Now just hold on a second," he said. "I know you had high hopes to get some of God's greatest plant, but you'll have to make do going out with our niece instead. Brenna Mae will be here any minute, now."

"Well, I'll be damned," I said, nervous as all hell to spend time with a woman my age, "pardon my language, ma'am, but I'd rather go out with a gal any night than smoke herb alone."

"For some reason, I don't believe you," said Elroy. "Way I remember, you preferred smoke over a drink."

"I would rather smoke than drink any night," I said.

"You know where the beers are," said Elroy, pointing to the empty bottles. "I refuse to be your beer fetch."

"All right, all right," I said. "Just take it easy, I know how you like to get bipolar."

Karen laughed, "He sure does."

Elroy smiled, "You'll do just fine as a civilian. Don't worry, I know your work ethic. And besides, you're a smart, strong young man with a solid head on your shoulders. Why don't you travel down to Latin America for a while, like you talked about? Meet a woman, buy a surfboard, spend a few months on a beach."

"Yeah, maybe," I said. "In the meantime, I need a cigarette."

"Go and see the world without a gun in your hands," said Karen.

"No shit." I walked outside to smoke to the subtle sound of dry leaves blowing on the street. Television light flashed from behind closed drapes in nearly every household. Stars twinkled.

"I don't know what to do," I said, back inside. "I have endless free time and my mind keeps racing and racing and racing and I don't know how to slow it down. I want to make up for lost years but know it's impossible."

"You cannot make up for lost time, dear," said Karen. "Once it is gone, it's gone. You will only lose more time trying to get it back. Live in the moment, it's all we have."

"This is a wise woman." Elroy hugged her and she blushed. "In my opinion," he said, "nothing heals the body and mind better than some old fashion lovemaking."

"Oh, Elroy," said Karen. "Behave yourself."

"Take a swim in the morning, eat fresh fruit for breakfast, and pray to God for forgiveness. After you've done that for about a year, reflect on what you went through and write it down. You were always writing something down. Take the good and carry it, and leave the bad behind. That's what you need to do, Bobby—go somewhere and reflect for a while. Away from friends and family, they will only distract you and tempt you with your old habits."

"I thought that I needed to be around people who love me," I said. "I'm confused."

"Like who, your old drinking buddies from high school?" He said. "Hell no."

"Go and be with your mother for a little while," said Karen. "Let her take care of you while you get used to your new life."

"Maybe," said Elroy, flicking his nose, "but, I think a person can only reflect when they are alone, otherwise they constantly gain new experiences and never have time."

I nodded then walked to the garage for two more. Elroy followed. He flipped on the light and pulled a tarp off a motorcycle he was building. "I cried for two days the first time I saw Pink Floyd," he said.

"You don't think that's overdoing it?"

"It blew my mind." He smiled. "That human beings working together could create such beauty. I will never doubt humans again."

His chest expanded and his voice lowered as he talked about the 1965 camouflage Royal Enfield with a sidecar.

"I thought you only liked Harleys?" I said.

"That's what I want people to think," he said. "It's all about the image. But let me tell ya, these old Enfields are like none other." He talked about the specs and I tuned him out. "I can't wait to finish this girl and ride into the deep south with Karen in the sidecar and a big bag of God's greatest in a saddlebag." He smiled. "It'll be the best time of my life." His eyes shined as he sat and grabbed the handlebars.

"I hope you do that, Elroy," I said. "You have to retire first."

He flicked the tip of his nose and rubbed his belly. "Soon enough."

I grabbed another beer, popped the lid with a lighter, and swallowed it half down.

"The limes are inside," he said.

"I don't need a fucking lime." I finished the bottle and opened another.

"You're hitting it hard tonight, ay Bobby?"

"Isn't that the point?"

He shrugged, swung his leg over the bike, and put his hand on my shoulder.

"You have only been free a couple of days now," he said. "Be patient—things will work out."

I finished the beer and pined for Elliot. We used to save coins to buy cheap bottles of vodka to mix with orange juice and drink in the public bathrooms. I wish she would have waited.

"Here's Brenna Mae," said Elroy. The sound of a vehicle interrupted my self-pity. "Let's go in and get you ready." He patted me on the shoulder and I did not move. "Be easy on yourself, Bobby, you're a good young man, don't forget it. You lived through hell so you can live in heaven," he said. "Have a long, healthy life."

"I don't want to think about war anymore," I said. "At least not for a while."

"You don't have to," he said. "The time to reflect will come later. For now, enjoy the moment."

He opened the door and I followed. A woman in her early twenties wearing a jean skirt and bright-yellow tank-top swung open the front door and walked straight to the bathroom.

"Hi, Brenna Mae," said Elroy.

"Hi," she replied while closing the bathroom door. She finished and walked up to me holding her hand out.

"You must be Bob," she said. "I'm Brenna Mae." We shook and she curtsied. "My Uncle told me all about you."

"Hopefully not too much," I said. "It's a pleasure to meet you."

Her hand was soft like an eagle feather, her red hair was professionally layered and dyed.

"I am your party partner for the night," she said. "Elroy asked me to take you out and show you a good time." I swayed, noticing her round face and a thick layer of make-up. She was no Elliot, but she smelled good. "Do you need to change into something else?" she said, looking me up and down. I was wearing black Carhartts, a black tee-shirt with a howling wolf, and a black Raiders hat. I shook my head. "I'm going to the bathroom to tidy up. It'll only be a few minutes, then we can go." I nodded. She hugged Elroy and Karen before going back to the bathroom. I tried not to stare at the backs of her thighs but couldn't help it. Her legs looked freshly shaven.

"That's a cool shirt," said Elroy. "Hey, since you didn't get me a Harley Davidson shirt in Croatia, maybe you can send me one when you get home."

"No problem," I said, slipping on my shoes and going out to smoke. Elroy followed.

"My niece has a little boy named Fergus," he said. "He is four and a half. She refuses to stop partying, and because of that, she lost custody." I lit a cigarette and watched the smoke rise.

"She works at a bank and makes decent money, yet continues to ask for more. She says it's for food, gas, and diapers, but I think she spends it partying."

"Why are you telling me this?" I said.

He shook his head, shrugged then flicked his nose while rubbing his belly. "She drives drunk all the time, then shows up to work half-cocked. Be careful," he said. "And look out for her, tonight. Would ya?"

"I'll do what I can," I said, "but she's a grown woman, so I won't physically restrain her."

"Of course not," he said. "Just do what you can to keep her out of trouble."

I nodded. "I have one question for you," I said.

"What's that?"

I finished my beer and handed him the bottle.

"Where am I sleeping tonight?"

He grabbed his stomach and laughed.

"Ah hell, Bobby, I am your brother, not your keeper. You'll sleep where you lay your head, hopefully, it's not in a ditch."

"Amen." I was too drunk to laugh.

Karen came outside to ask if I wanted a peanut butter and jelly sandwich for the road. "It would be good to eat something," she said. "You might get sick."

"I'm feeling good and don't want to ruin it," I said. "Thank you, though."

"Okay, then," she said, "just be careful tonight."

Brenna Mae stormed outside.

"You ready?" she asked.

"Ready as I'll ever be."

"Let's go." She walked to the vehicle without saying goodbye.

"All right, brother," I said. "Thanks for everything."

"We'll grab breakfast with my father in the morning," he said.

"It's a plan."

"Have fun," said Karen. "It's been a pleasure getting to know you better. God bless you."

"God doesn't know me."

I stumbled to the idling Ford Explorer and climbed in. She was listening to Wu-Tang's 36 Chambers too loud to talk as we whizzed out of the neighborhood onto the main strip, racing around in search of the busiest bar. I glanced at her knee caps, thighs, and cleavage and wondered if she was disease-free. She turned down the music twice to talk on the phone before turning it back up. It was annoying; she thought I didn't have anything to say, so I stared out the window watching lights fly by. After 4 or 5 passes, she chose the loudest bar where "Bombs Over Baghdad" blasted from wide-open doors and windows. I laughed. People stumbled on the sidewalk, others swayed on the balcony. Everybody was talking and laughing. I kept a straight face while scanning for weapons and threats. All was clear, for now. I tried to keep up. She hugged the bouncer who asked for my ID and I showed my military ID before going up narrow stairs to the second floor. It was obvious Brenna Mae didn't give a shit about me, why would she? I was an evil man.

We found a booth in the corner where two of her girlfriends were drinking long island ice teas with glossy eyes. They were done up like girls in magazines, and they looked me up and down like a piece of trash they refuse to pick up. Neither said hello.

"You want a drink?" I asked Brenna Mae and she ignored me. I asked again and she denied it, insisting on buying the first round. I felt bad about taking her son's food money but what the hell, I followed her to the bar and asked for a double Jameson on the rocks. She nodded, so I went through the crowd of staring people to hide in the bathroom.

"What the fuck am I doing?" I asked myself in the mirror. My eyes were bloodshot and ugly. "Just be cool," I said. "Be cool." I splashed water on my face and took a leak leaning against the wall.

Back at the booth, she handed me the drink and we touched glasses. She didn't give a shit about cheers, she didn't give a damn about me. I stood at the end of the table feeling like a creep. The girls laughed about something I could not hear because their voices were low and the music loud, so I went outside on the balcony to drink and smoke alone. I wanted to be alone by a campfire, but I was stuck.

The women wanted nothing to do with me, and I could understand why. I thought. I was a fucking piece of shit, a terrorizer. I brought only harm to people and deserved no love and affection. I will never feel the camaraderie again, I thought. I miss Sully and Brammer; I miss my brothers.

I smoked a few cigarettes and watched cars pass below, wanting to either jump and die or toss a grenade and laugh at the destruction.

Back at the table, the girls were laughing with three well-dressed men squeezed into the booth. They acted like they didn't see me so I returned to the bar to order another whiskey before going back to the roof guard position.

Nobody wants to hear about burnt children with missing limbs, I thought. Nobody wants to talk about the kid with elephantiasis on a chain in the yard. Maybe they want to hear about the rush that comes when the bullets stop and you grab your dick and realize it's still there. Nobody wants to hear about the time I stabbed my mini-DVD player to death because it finally stopped working and it was my only escape.

I left the balcony to try mingling inside but didn't say anything to anybody so I went to the bathroom to hide in the stall for a few minutes before gaining the courage to talk with Brenna Mae.

I ordered a round of long island ice teas for Brenna Mae and the girls, set them on the edge of the table without saying a word, and walked off.

I wanted to tell them that I had just returned from Iraq, in hopes of congratulations, a hug, or a thank you, but I didn't know how to talk to women. I staggered onto the balcony to smoke and feel light rainfall.

I was guilty of being part of a catastrophic force that bombed cities, towns, and villages. Guilty of forcing people to wait in hundred and thirty degrees heat in barbed wire lines for water and propane. Guilty of yelling at peaceful families after kicking in their door as they slept, ending their dreams with flashlights and loaded guns in their faces. Men, women, and children, it didn't matter. Everybody was shoved and searched. Nobody wants to hear my fucking sob story, so I'll keep it to myself. I went to the bathroom stall after stealing a pen and napkin from the bar and scribbled frantically with a shaky hand.

My baby fat cheeks flush with embarrassment—
"Sorry my gun is in your face- you see-
I'm terrified you will try to kill me. Are you hiding
explosives under your hijab? Take it off!
Oh, you can't understand me? Here, let me help you...
Please don't scream—It's only hair, I won't get
turned on by your hair alone—I swear.
You people smell funny anyway. Please don't cry—It's
only temporary, your husband will be back in a few days
or weeks or years. Please stop screaming! Don't make me
push you on the floor and put my boot on your back,
You fucking bitch. Shut the fuck up! Go stand
in the corner with your forehead to the wall and
back to the room! Go! Know your place."
My cheeks are sunken with malnutrition of spirit,
mind, and body. I cannot eat enough, exercise
enough, pray enough or take enough vitamins
to become healthy and free from guilt.

When I returned to the table, it was covered in glasses and Brenna Mae was dancing on the seat even though she was wearing a short skirt. The guys mean mugged me and I wanted to shoot them in the face. The women avoided eye contact. I went to the bar for another double whiskey, tipped ten bucks, then swirled it around to hear ice clinking on the glass. It reminded me of glaciers back home, I wished I were there so bad. I went back to the porch and Brenna Mae came out to see why I was drinking alone. I told her that I had just stepped out, and she looked around at everything but me. She pulled out her cell phone to text somebody.

"Let's go somewhere else," she said, staring at the screen.

"Whatever you want," I said. "This is your town."

"After this drink," she said, holding a full long island iced tea.

"Where are we going?"

"Not sure." Her fingers moved quickly on the phone. "I'll drive."

"We should get a cab," I said. "I'll pay."

"I need my car in the morning," she said. "To get to work."

"Let's call Elroy," I said. "He would pick us up and give you a ride in the morning."

She laughed and looked at me, "I'm not calling my fucking uncle right now. If you want to stay, stay. I don't give a shit."

I turned my attention to a handful of moths on a street lamp.

"I'll come," I said, quietly.

"I'm going to finish my drink with my girls," she said. "Then I'll be ready."

She flicked the cigarette onto the street below and I watched her bare legs move, admiring the backs of her knees. By the time we left the bar, I hadn't talked to a single person besides her.

Wu-Tang was still too loud to talk in the car, and I tried to distract myself from focusing on her swerving, speeding driving. So I thought about her child being raised by somebody else, and I wondered how much money was spent tonight on drinks and smokes that could have gone elsewhere. I was toasted and deep in self-pity by the time we arrived at the next bar. Brenna Mae had used her child's food money to buy this murderer another drink. I found a table in a dark corner to sit alone while watching the crowd and she went from person to person. We left after one drink, Brenna Mae decided that we should go back to her place so she could get to sleep early and be ready for work. She sped down backroads through neighborhoods, swerving onto a bike path while trying to change the song. I was too drunk to focus, one-eyed drunk.

Where will I sleep, tonight? I wondered. She reached over to turn down the music.

"Do you want to stay at my place?"

"Does a bear shit in the woods?" I mumbled incoherently.

"What did you say?"

"Nothing," I nodded and tried to smile.

She turned up the music and we bumped through quiet neighborhoods until pulling into her driveway. I tried to follow her inside but she speed-walked and I stumbled, eventually, I made it indoors with a couple of near falls on the lawn.

"Make yourself comfortable," she said. "I need a shower."

I couldn't help but admire her smooth, shiny legs and long, clean hair as she walked toward the restroom. I staggered around the living room and kitchen with a glass of water while looking at framed photographs of people on the wall. I was nervous about being alone with a woman, it had been so long. She came out of the bathroom in a tight pink tank top without a bra and a pair of tiny pink shorts.

"My God," I said.

"What?" she curtsied, "I'm getting in bed. It's already two and I have to wake up at six-thirty. If you want to sleep with me, you can, just come in whenever you're ready."

She stretched her arms above her head and stood on her tiptoes. Her nipples pressed against cotton and her calves and thighs flexed. She turned a one-eighty and her round butt was so tight I wanted to know it. She went into the bedroom as I rinsed my face and mouth in the kitchen sink.

"You got this," I said. "It'll be okay. Just relax."

I entered her room and waited for my eyes to adjust. I felt a tinge of fear, remembering my childhood baseball coach, I approached the bed cautiously. Inching over to it while feeling like a burglar or a creep or a born-again virgin.

"You don't have to be so quiet," she said. "I'm still awake."

"Oh, okay." I stood at the edge of the bed, unsure if I should take off my clothes.

"Are you sleeping in your clothes?"

"I don't know," I said. "I don't have underwear."

"Do what makes you comfortable."

She rustled under the blankets as I stripped off my clothes and stood naked in the dark. What the hell would Elroy say? I thought. She lifted the blanket and I slid inside. Before I could get settled, her smooth legs wrapped around mine and pulled me close. The smell of shampoo and soap was intoxicating. She began rubbing my stomach and chest with her left hand while moving her leg over my privates.

"Do you have a condom?" she said.

"No," I said. "Do you?"

"No."

"Fuck it," I said. "Who uses condoms anyway?"

"It's late," she said. "And I need sleep."

She moved her hand down my stomach and played with my pubic hair.

"But," I said, my body tense. "I want you."

"And I want you," she said. "So, I'll do what I do best."

She kissed my cheek, rolled over, and began snoring in no time.

24

The next morning, Brenna Mae hit snooze three times before rushing out of bed and dashing around the room.

"That was fun last night," she said.

"Uh-huh."

"It was great to meet you," she said. "Drive safe. I hope to see you again."

I slept until nine-thirty, took a shower, then followed a map to Elroy's she had drawn and left on the counter.

"Look what the cat dragged in," said Elroy, drinking coffee next to Karen on the front steps.

I forced a smile, I was hungover and hungry.

"Good morning," said Karen. "How was last night?"

"It was okay," I said, rubbing my eyes. "Uneventful."

"Did Brenna Mae drive home drunk?" Elroy asked.

"Would you like a cup of coffee?" offered Karen.

"Please," I said. "I need a cup of coffee."

She walked inside with help from her cane.

Elroy stared at me waiting for a response.

"Yeah," I said, "she drove drunk."

"Dammit!" He kicked a pebble and flicked his nose. "I knew it."

"I tried to stop her," I said, "but I couldn't physically take the keys."

"I know, I know."

"At least we both made it home alive," I said. "And it sure is a nice morning." I pointed at the fluffy clouds covering the blue sky and listened to the few remaining leaves clinging to the trees in the light breeze.

"I wish she would think about little Fergus," he said. "The poor kid has a shit storm of a mother."

Karen opened the door with a mug in her hand. I took it and thanked her.

"I wish every parent would put their kids as priority number one," she said. "Instead of treating them like tomatoes from Taco Bell."

We laughed at the analogy.

"So," said Elroy, smirking. "Did you two have fun?"

"It was all right," I said. "We went to a couple of bars then back to her place. It was uneventful."

"She sure enjoys the bars," said Karen. "I don't understand it, the music is too loud to have a decent conversation."

"It's not about the conversation, ma," said Elroy, gyrating his hips. "It's about the fornication."

We all laughed.

"Oh, Elroy," she said. "Will you grow up?"

"Never, Mama." He kissed her cheek. "Hey, Bobby, my Dad and I eat at the same place every Saturday and Sunday when I'm in town. Are you hungry?"

"I'm famished," I said. "After my coffee, I'm ready."

"Give me a couple of minutes." He kissed Karen's hair and then went inside.

"He doesn't want to ask about details," she said, smiling. "And neither do I."

"There aren't any details to share," I said. "Do you have any plans for the day?"

"Nothing more complicated than enjoying being alive in the comfort of my home," she said.

"That sounds pleasant."

"It's all about the little things," she said. "Like making new friends, staying connected with old friends, and carving out time for prayer. It has been a great pleasure to meet you," she said, "Elroy was right about you; you are a bright young man with unlimited potential."

Elroy came out and touched Karen's shoulders.

"Leave your mug," he said, taking it from my hands and setting it by Karen's slippered feet. "I love you, Ma, and I'll see you in a couple of hours."

I shot down the coffee, thanked and hugged Karen, and said goodbye. I followed Elroy slowly through the neighborhood until we parked in front of his favorite diner. A bell rang after we entered and two waitresses said good morning simultaneously.

"Good morning Pa, I would like you to meet a young man I served with."

His father stood from a booth in the corner and held out a strong, wrinkled hand.

"His name is Bob Stark," said Elroy.

"He was one heck of a soldier."

"It's a pleasure to meet you," said Elroy's father. We shook to the smell of coffee and maple syrup. "The name's Leroy, Leroy Longhorn."

"The honor is mine, sir."

"Bob was discharged a couple of days ago," said Elroy. "He is on his way home to the great state of Alaska."

"Is that right?"

"Yes sir," I said. "Thankfully I drive an old lemon, otherwise—I would probably have a few speeding tickets by now."

We laughed.

"Whereabouts in Alaska are you from?"

"I was raised in Nome, sir. Lived there until I was eight or nine before moving to a suburb of Anchorage called Eagle River. I lived there until high school when my family moved to Seward. I graduated from there."

"I haven't been up there," he said. "But I've studied the maps. I would sure love to go one day. You headed there now?"

"No sir, first I'm going to Arizona to visit my mother. We planned a little road trip to visit some family in Idaho, and spend some time along the Pacific coast."

"Sounds monumental," he said. "I guarantee she missed you."

The waitress came over to take our order. She was happy to see Elroy and asked him how long he was back in town and when he was finally going to retire from the military and move home. He laughed, flicked his nose, and said, "You never can tell." Elroy and his father had the same red nose and small forehead, hard bellies, slightly hunched backs, thick hands, thick fingers, and thick shoulders with perfectly straight, white teeth. Oh, and really big, genuine smiles with patient brown eyes full of understanding. I noticed Leroy had a Louis L'amour book beneath his right hand. The waitress left with our orders after filling up our drinks.

"The most important thing a young man like yourself can do," said Leroy. "If they are lucky enough to make it home from the war alive and they aren't too shell shocked from the hell they lived through, is to explore and fall in love with the country they fought for. Otherwise, it may seem like they fought for nothing."

Elroy and I nodded.

"It is easy to understand why a young war veteran might feel a certain level of anger toward his country," he said. "And towards God and his fellow human beings, after seeing men at their worst." I was on the edge of my seat. "The honest to God truth is—the majority of Americans, and all human beings, are good and simple people who are doing what they were taught while trying to find some level of happiness. We cannot hate them or judge them for doing what they were taught, even if it is wrong and harmful. We must never forget that."

"Yes sir," I said.

Elroy patted his father's shoulder. "My pa here earned two silver stars and three purple hearts in World War II."

"Wow," I said.

Leroy bowed his head, took a drink of coffee, and examined his hands.

"He stormed the beaches of Normandy," said Elroy. "He was one of the first men on Omaha."

"And what you are doing is exactly what I had to do when I returned home," said Leroy. "I packed a duffel in a car and hit the road. I spent nearly three years traveling from Maine to Florida, six months going from Florida to California, two years going from California to Washington, and an entire year on the Hawaiian Islands. Only God knows what kind of trouble I got into out there."

We all laughed, I almost cried.

"I came to believe that God blessed our country and every one of the citizens," he said. "Old and new, black, white, red and yellow. We are united under one flag. I haven't been to Alaska, though, maybe before I die."

Elroy and I laughed while Leroy kept a straight face. He looked in my eyes with tenderness and understanding, like he, too, lived with heartache and guilt; like he, too, had hidden wounds. I wanted to hear his life story, but there was not enough time. The food came out. We ate and fueled up on coffee, as I told them of my dreams to travel to Latin America, learn Spanish and visit Mayan temples, and eventually buy a piece of property in Alaska to farm and write.

"You want to be a writer and a farmer?" said Leroy.

"Yes sir," I said.

"Those are perfect jobs for a war veteran," he said. "They go together like butter and potatoes. Both are healing endeavors as ancient as man. Work the soil in the summer and the soul in the winter. You will do well, I can tell."

"Thank you, sir," I said. "Thank you both for everything."

"Do you know much about farming?" Asked Leroy.

"Not the first thing," I said.

They both laughed. "You sound like an infantryman to me, always doing things the hard way," said Leroy. "I'm sure you'll get it figured out. Don't forget to use the ashes from your wood stove on your potatoes, they work wonders."

I watched and envied the father and son team interact like best friends. Laughing, joking, and nudging each other; they patted shoulders and finished sentences.

"How is your relationship with your father?" Asked Leroy.

I paused to watch the clouds. "I don't know him," I said, and stood up. "I need to use the restroom, please excuse me."

I washed and stared in the mirror imagining what Leroy went through in Europe during World War II. I wondered if it was similar to Vonnegut, or worse.

Maybe if I could stay away from the bottle, I thought, and away from self-pity, I could be an old man reading a Louis L'amour novel in a diner while waiting on his kid.

When I returned to the table, Elroy was tucking away his wallet. He thanked me for taking care of Brenna Mae, hugged me, and rubbed my shoulders. Leroy shook my hand

and thanked me for my service. I laughed and thanked him. They both told me to drive safe and be patient with life, I was young, and they reminded me, although I felt ancient. I thanked the waitress, before walking outside to hit the road.

The sun was punching through the clouds, and I wondered if the sky ever ends. I was on the right path, I thought, Leroy reminded me of that. I started the Subaru and Bob Dylan's "Eve of Destruction" came over the speakers. I wished the eject button worked, instead, I was stuck with the same mix for thousands of miles. So I turned off the music and lit a cigarette, I needed some silence.

I left Arkansas and was driving through fields and prairies in Oklahoma with the windows down and a warm breeze blowing away all my worries. I spotted a hitchhiker in the distance and wondered if it was my father. I passed him to see his face then pulled over and watched him run.

He was balding with a goatee, wearing faded blue jeans with holes in the knees, dirty white sneakers, and an unbuttoned blue flannel. He was five-seven or five-eight, a hundred and forty or so pounds. The small amount of hair he had on his head was long, gray, and thin.

"Where you headed?" I asked, searching his bloodshot eyes for evil intent.

"West," he said, with a hoarse voice. "I'm headed west." He smelled like vodka and cigarette butts. I smelled like whiskey and cigarette butts.

"Perfect, me too." I motioned towards the back of the car. "Find a place for your bag and let's go."

He glanced in back then sat in the passenger seat with his small pack between his feet.

"You sure have a lot of stuff back there," he said.

"Nothing but memories," I said. "I like to carry them around with me. I'm learning to let go."

"I know the feeling."

He took a deep breath and looked out the window.

"Where are you coming from?" I said.

"Key West," he said. "I've been living and working there for a few years now."

"Key West is all right," I said, "a little too ritzy for me, though. What were you doing?"

"I'm an airplane mechanic," he said. "Have been for thirty years." He sat straighter and stuck his chest out. "Too many rich folks with private planes want to underpay a mechanic."

"Is that right?"

He picked at the holes in his knees. "Yes sir," he said. "Ain't it a shame that only rich assholes can afford to live in the most beautiful places in America? I was never in the top one percent or nothing like that, but I was certainly a greedy rich guy for a while. So I understand why they do things the way they do."

"No offense," I said. "But you don't come off as being a greedy rich guy."

He laughed heartily.

"It's God's honest truth," he said. "I ain't no liar."

"Let's hear the story," I said. "If you don't mind."

He took a wheezy breath, coughed, then hawked up

something and spat out the window. He sat in silence for a minute, and I noticed that he was an ageless man, anywhere between thirty and sixty-five. He noticed the dozens of empty packs of cigarettes on the dashboard and then asked if he could smoke.

"Go ahead," I said.

He pulled out a big bag of pipe tobacco, rolled a smoke, and lit it.

"I lived in Seattle for twenty-seven years working for Alaska Airlines," he said. "Making more money than I knew what to do with, like Scrooge from the Duck Tales, remember that show?"

"Yes sir," I said. "He kept gold coins in a swimming pool and swam in them every day."

"That's right," he said. "I had a pretty wife and a good kid, a couple of flashy cars, and a 4,700 square foot house full of handmade furniture, fine art, and artifacts from around the world. I had a music room with more instruments than The Eagles. We had everything an American family could want and more."

"Oh wow."

"The only problem—was that life lacked a crucial ingredient."

"Which is?"

"Fun," he said. "Family life wasn't enough. Baseball games, parent-teacher conferences, and dinner dates were all lifeless and boring. Once our kid was born, the wife and mine's relationship was put on the back burner, and there it stayed.

Eventually, I started drinking alone in the music room and would end up with my buddies at the topless bar. I only drank top-shelf bourbon though, so I didn't think I had a problem." He paused to pull out his wallet. "This is my son. It's a picture from ten years ago."

"He was a good-looking kid," I said.

"I started dating a dancer who supplied me with endless cocaine and sex," he said. "We ran hard." He hung his head and picked his dry knees. "After losing every fucking thing I had, I look back with so much regret it's hard to go on. I quit drinking too many times to count, but it doesn't last, it never fucking lasts. This time, though, it's different, I'm staying sober and going back to Seattle to win back my family. To show them that I cleaned up."

"How long have you been sober?"

"Forty-nine days," he said.

"That's a while!" I said. "More power to you. I don't think I could quit drinking."

"I have been to thousands of meetings across the country but can't seem to stay sober longer than fifty days. I had a homegroup and sponsor and all in Key West, but nothing could make me not take the first drink. Nothing. I called my sponsor when I felt the urge and he would try to talk me out of it but nobody can, not even myself. And when I start, I can't stop, I'll disappear for days. 'Time traveling,' I call it. I'll come out of it somewhere else and won't remember a damn thing."

"I know the feeling," I said.

"I miss being a kid," he said. "I want to be a kid again." I nodded, trying to follow his jumpy dialogue. "Whatever happened to building snowmen and sandcastles just to melt and wash away? Can't we just stack rocks on the beach for the hell of it?"

"We can," I said. "If we take the time."

"That's what I'm talking about," he said. "Like my friend, Dagger Dan, says, 'Nothing more nothing less, I'm sick and tired of this fucked up mess.' The problems with my family exceeded rapidly until eventually there was a climax."

"What happened?"

"I was working graveyards at the hangar while the wife worked days at the office. We never saw each other. The house would be empty when I got off work around nine. With the kid at school and the wife at work, I didn't know what to do. I was lonely, bored, and rich, a deadly trifecta. I had the American dream, yet I still was miserable. It was a hard realization." He hung his head, rolled another cigarette, and lit it. "I cheated on her too many times to remember," he said. "I placed ads online for women to travel with on weekends to Vegas, at my expense, of course. With free flight benefits, all I had to do was pay for a room, food, and drink, and then I'd give them a thousand bucks or so to gamble. Hell, then I could do anything I wanted to them. You should've seen me when I was younger, I looked just like James Dean."

"I did that for years without the wife knowing. Until she asked me to quit spending so much time alone and to spend more time with the family. I tried, oh God I tried, but it didn't work. I always got bored, and by that time I was a full-blown addict so I couldn't go without drugs or alcohol for longer than a few hours. I was, what they say, 'Restless, irritable, and discontent.' I didn't realize that I had a problem; I mean, my friends were heavy drinkers who used cocaine regularly and I was no worse. Hell, they were upstanding citizens! But the wife continued to nag. She said that I had a problem and that I needed help or to find another place to live. So I started going to meetings in Federal Way, but as I said, I can't put together more than fifty days."

"It was the third day of a bender when my girlfriend and I were higher than a Cessna on pills and bourbon; we loved chasing pills with bourbon." He smiled. "We called it: 'The Atomic Chaser.' Anyway, we went to her work at the club to drink and watch the girls dance. Everybody knew us down there. It feels good to be somewhere where everybody knows your name. The strangers looked at me like I was Ted Danson or something from *Cheers*. The problem with the pills was that anywhere between five to seven hours later, you pass out stone cold no matter where you are."

"Oh no," I said. "That's a dangerous side effect."

"It takes some real strategizing," he said. "You get used to it, though. It's like what them boys are dealing with in Iraq right now. You can get used to anything until it changes. We left the club in my Lexus, I thought it would be fun to cruise Highway 1. She asked me not to, but I didn't care what she said. She wasn't good for nothing anyway. Ha! To paraphrase the police report, I 'passed out at the wheel going ninety-five in a thirty-five.' I woke up in jail when the pills wore off." He laughed, coughed, and spat.

"Did you total the car?" I said. "Did your girlfriend survive?"

"I totaled the car all right," he said. "I smashed into a fucking house. The officer in the pen told me what happened and offered me a phone call. So I called my girlfriend, she had taken the drugs and cash and fled the scene. She said that she couldn't wake me up no matter how hard she tried, but I don't believe her, the bitch. She just wanted to steal the money and drugs are all. She had some scrapes and cuts," he said, "but nothing serious."

"You guys were lucky," I said.

"Lucky," he said and laughed, "I don't think so. Bail was set at a thousand dollars, so she came to pick me up later that day. We had a quickie at the house before she left, and I never saw her again. I was sitting in that big ol' house all alone, so I figured, 'What the hell, it's twelve-o'clock somewhere,' and I pulled out the bottle of rum and started blasting some White Snake."

"Something about rum makes me feel like I'm floating in the Caribbean," he said. "But after no time, the bottle was empty and I needed more. With the wife in Cincinnati for a conference and the kid with his grandma in Port Townsend, I found the key to her Mercedes and went to the corner store."

"No biggy, but on the way home, as I was turning the last fucking bend into the neighborhood, the car lost traction and flew off the road."

I shook my head at his misfortune.

"I drove to that damn store thousands of times without an accident," he said. "But that night, my higher power, that's what they say in the meetings, wanted my run to end. He has another plan for me. The Mercedes flew off the road like a jet, and got high centered on a rock in the neighbor's lawn." He laughed. "You should have seen their fucking faces. Ha! I revved the engine like a mother fucker trying to get off that damn thing but the wheels just spun and spun and spun. So I grabbed the bottle and sprinted to the house and hid in the basement."

He stared at the floorboard and rolled another smoke.

"The doorbell rang hundreds of times but I didn't answer. I wanted it all to go away. At some point, I passed out. And when I woke up, my wife was screaming with an officer by her side. I didn't remember anything. She told me about the Mercedes, the rock, and that everybody in the neighborhood had watched. 'Everybody knows about the sex and drugs' she said."

He hung his head, lit another smoke, and wiped his eyes.

"I was handcuffed and taken to jail," he whispered. "I haven't seen my wife or kid since."

"How long ago was that?" I said.

"Ten years," he said. "Ten long years. My brother offered me a job cleaning swimming pools in Key West, so I took him up on it. Can you believe it, an airplane mechanic making a living cleaning swimming pools? It hasn't been easy finding work after I was dragged across the coals by the American judicial system. Ah hell, don't get me started!"

I dodged a crater in the road while a knot formed in my throat.

"They say that time heals all wounds," he said. "It has been enough time. My boy is seventeen or eighteen, maybe nineteen now. I refused to sign the divorce papers, so my wife is still my wife. They must've forgiven me by now."

I didn't have anything to say, so I smoked in silence. I suddenly wanted him out of the car so bad I felt furious. Was it because he resembled me in the future if I kept drinking? Was it because he reminded me of my father, who I consistently hoped in the deep dark recesses of my mind would one day reach out to me and tell me he was proud of me and want a relationship? I do not know, but a sudden feeling of rage came over me.

"I don't know if I'll ever find what I'm searching for," he said. "It's like, only children can have fun," he said. "Their minds aren't tainted by drugs, dreams, desires. All of this God damn competition brings everybody down. Things will be okay when I'm around my kid again, and I need to make amends to the wife. Let me tell ya, kid, don't ever get stuck in a boring, mechanical existence. Work and money, work and money; wrenching screws, nuts, and bolts, they'll turn you fucking loose." He took a few deep breaths. "Do you know the old saying: 'Work and money won't keep your honey?'"

I shook my head. "Never heard it."

"Well, now you have," he said. "Don't forget it."

When we arrived at the nearest gas station, I said that I was going to grab a bite. I dropped him off in the back and snuck around the corner back onto the highway.

I drove across Texas into New Mexico hypnotized by large stacks of red rocks called hoodoos. Hours, minutes, and miles slipped by as I drove and drove and drove, taking in the large valleys and vast dry landscapes. I took naps, made pit stops, and smoked my way over the highlands and the Continental Divide until finally reaching Coolidge only a few days after leaving Kentucky. I swore to one day return to New Mexico for further exploration.

Mother worked at the only Safeway in town right off Main Street in the same parking lot as Blockbuster and Auto Zone. Heat waves rose from the concrete parking lot. It was just after two and I was nervous to see my mother after having been through so much. Two Hispanic families spoke Spanish while walking toward the entrance, I wished I could understand them. I saw Mother at a check stand, she was assisting an employee with an override while a very large couple with a cart full of two-liter sodas, chips, hot dogs, meat, candy, and two donuts breathed heavily while sweating. I watched from a few feet behind, hearing her calm voice while seeing her brought great comfort. I hadn't seen her in over two years and she looked great. Her hair was to her lower back and strawberry blonde, and she was leaner than I had ever seen her. She finished her task and scanned for the next project, it was my cue. I hugged her from behind and she started laughing.

"Welcome home son," she said. "It's my son everybody… it's my son…" She turned and kissed my lips and hugged me and wouldn't let go. Taking my hand, she rushed me around the store to introduce me to her coworkers. People thanked me for my service and told me what a wonderful mother I had. Mother glowed. A lady gave me an egg roll. I felt like I was glowing.

We ate Chinese food in the break room and talked about our upcoming road trip. She was shaking with excitement. She gave me the directions and code to her trailer park before we hugged and I left.

It didn't take long to realize that Mother was the hot babe on the block in her trailer park. Two old men wore visors and drank beer while parked beside each other in golf carts. Two women in visors and sunglasses walked the fence. They stared curiously and I waved, they waved back. Had they always found time to walk and talk, or was that part of retirement?

The following days were spent practicing what Kerouac called 'the art of do-nothing.' What bliss it was. Mother worked and visited while I slept, watched movies, smoked, skateboarded, and ate. She had stocked the house with cherries, cheese dip, cereal, ice cream, and everything else she knew I loved. I found a couple of stair sets and gaps and a skate park to pass the time until our trip and to stay focused on the present instead of the past. I felt like a teenager again, without all the resentment and angst, I felt pretty good. I used the swimming pool to practice holding my breath underwater and to cool down. I visited Victor a couple of times who claimed to be truly worried about me while I was in Iraq. He was celebratory that I had returned without any physical injuries. In the evenings, Mother and I sat on lawn chairs drinking Corona with lime while watching the sunset. Arizona has some fiery red, epic sunsets.

Her friends, Brenda and Paul, came over to hang out and barbecue. It was comforting to see Brenda again, she had lived above us in Bayside Apartments in Seward and had been my mother's friend for years. Even though we weren't best friends or anything, it brought me the feeling of being home. Paul was easy to be around; humble and well-spoken, his presence brought peace and comfort. I didn't have to talk much when I was around these people, they chatted non-stop and I kept myself in the present moment.

I woke up one morning in the driver's seat of my car with the window wide open and puke running down the door. I vaguely remembered going to a Mexican dive bar where I danced with two older women who bought me tequila shots. How I made it home, only God knows? Two old women in a golf cart woke me up by asking if I was okay. I nodded. I wasn't okay. I was embarrassed. I didn't want to talk around Mother because I was so full of rage and self-pity for what I had done in Iraq that I felt like I would either cry or yell and I didn't want to do either, so I stayed straight-faced and acted calm even though my insides were on fire. This, in turn, made me want to run away so I could feel rather than hide. Of course, I couldn't say any of this to the old ladies or my mother, I just acted like everything was good.

It was easy to stay distracted from my thoughts and feelings by focusing on Mother's excitement about our upcoming trip. It was our first trip together since I was a little boy and her first vacation since who knows when. I had been there three days before she signed out on vacation and said goodbye to Victor. We packed the Pontiac with the necessities, changed the oil, and filled the tires, and we were ready.

"The last time I felt like this was when I was a little girl," she said. "When I used to ride with my daddy all over the country in his big rig."

"He was a truck driver?" I asked. My knowledge of my grandfather was limited, at best.

"Before the war," she said. "He was everything before the war."

"I'm glad to see you're excited," I said. "I am, too." We studied a map of Arizona on the kitchen table while eating ice cream with a movie in the background. "What time do you want to leave tomorrow?" I asked. Her eyes sparkled and she held her hands together and moved her fingers like she does when she's thinking. "I know you love early mornings."

She laughed and blushed.

"For us to watch the sunrise in Sedona," she said. "We have to leave here around four."

"Four in the morning?" I said, teasing. "Jesus, Mom, the only people up at that hour are monks and madmen."

She laughed, "And your Mama! We don't want to miss it."

"Okay, but, only if you drive."

"You know how much I love to drive," she said. "I'll prepare the coffee tonight so tomorrow all we have to do is push the button." We clinked spoons and ate. "I'm so glad you made it home safe, son," she said. "I was worried sick about you."

I had no response.

We ate portobello mushroom burgers and veggie shish kebabs earlier that evening, washing them down with red wine and Corona. I forgot about the war temporarily, about everything besides the moment. Paul came over and confessed that he was seventy-nine, I refused to believe him.

"Are you really that old," I said, "or do you use that line to pick up middle-aged women?"

He let out a deep bellied laugh.

"Why would an old man like me go and lie about his age?" He said. "You don't think we have better things to do?" He had short hair and a clean shave. "It's all about lifestyle," he continued. "Some of my friends are obese with stress and calories. They owe hundreds of thousands on homes and vehicles and debt, which keeps them working jobs they don't like. We're talking about people in their fifties, sixties, and seventies here. Not your age! I escaped all that. So, I live a simple life, have an old truck that runs well, and a small house for me and my dog. Everything's paid off. I don't drink or eat to excess and continue to help people and make a little bit of money by doing handyman work. Heck, maybe it's paid off over the years."

We went to bed early that night. I curled up on the floor in front of the television to distract myself from my thoughts, and in what seemed like a couple of hours, mother tiptoed into the kitchen to brew coffee.

We filled our to-go mugs, double-checked the essentials, and left. It was a brisk, desert morning, not even the birds and bugs were awake.

"The only people up at this hour are dairy farmers and drug addicts," I said.

"And us," said mother, laughing. The clock glowed at 3:58.

"How are you doing, Ma?"

"I am great, son," she said, sipping black coffee and smiling. "You know how I love to drive. It feels different to not have an agenda."

"Good different?" I asked.

"Definitely," she said, "I can't remember the last time."

"Me neither," I said, "but I need it."

"I wish your brother was here," she said. "I sure miss him."

"Me too," I said. "How is he?"

"You know your brother," she said. "He's ornerier than ever, although he seems to like his job at the brewery in Juneau."

"That's good," I said. "I'll have to visit when I get back."

"Yeah, but you know how I worry," she said. "And I'm worried about his drinking."

"Well he works at a brewery, what do you expect?"

"I know, I know."

I wondered what it was like to be married to a prisoner doing a life sentence without parole? If all of her dreams in life were coming true? She put in a Bob Seger CD and played *Turn the Page*, singing along to her favorite song. I turned my head to wipe a tear, I had missed her so much.

"We've only been gone an hour yet I already feel like I'm loosening up," she said.

"Me too, the last thing I want to do is spend thousands on hotel rooms," I said.

"Same here," she said. "I don't have more than a few hundred for the trip."

"I've got money, ma," I said. "Don't worry about that."

"I owe you almost twenty-thousand for helping me move from Alaska to Arizona during your first tour," she said. "I can't take any more of your money."

"You carried me for nine months, gave birth to me, raised me, and dealt with my bullshit in high school. You don't owe me anything."

"Besides," she said, "do you think that just because I'm almost fifty I'm some kind of wuss?"

"No ma'am," I said, laughing. "I would never think you're a wuss. With the money we save, we could fund our next trip."

"And I've got bills to pay," she said.

"Don't think about your bills, Ma, we're on vacation."

We laughed.

"I'll sleep in the front seat tonight," she said, "and the next night we'll rotate. How's that sound?"

"I can sleep in front the whole time," I said.

"That wouldn't be fair."

"But it would be fine."

"No way, son, let's rotate."

"Whatever you say, Ma, you're the boss. At least let me take the front seat tonight."

It was settled.

She timed the drive to Sedona perfectly. We parked by a massive rock formation as the sun crested the horizon casting thousands of shades of red. We stepped outside into cool desert air, I lit a cigarette and noticed a man crouched behind a tripod with his eye pressed to the viewfinder. I envied him. Why didn't I become obsessed with taking pictures instead of shooting targets? Was he a former sniper? Was it too late? What passions did I have and pursue? The colors on the rocks changed every moment and he moved angles to best capture them. After a few minutes, he methodically packed his gear into a brand new Subaru and left.

Mother was changing angles and taking pictures with a big smile. I smoked and stared. We went to a tourist center and found a trail map to the vortexes. I cannot describe the energy at the vortexes, but I can say this, we hiked past hundreds of stacks of rocks to every vortex on the map and at each one, I laid down and quickly fell asleep, though I did not feel tired at all. Mother claimed that it was the healing energy of the Earth mending my wounds. I am not sure what it was, but I know one thing, I felt tranquility for the first time in years.

We left town after dark-headed north towards the Grand Canyon. Pulling off at a pizza parlor, we ate dinner then found a rest area and made our beds.

"How did it feel to be in Sedona again, Ma," I said, finding comfort in the front seat, "as good as the first time?"

"You're darn rights," she said. It was her favorite saying. "The energy is so powerful, I feel rejuvenated."

"And we hiked our butts off," I said. "Are you tired?"

She chuckled. "A little bit. I feel something more than just tired, something deeper. There is great healing power in the vortexes, son. You just have to believe it."

"Yeah, there's something to them," I said. "That's for sure."

"I love you, son," she said, from her bed in the back. "I'm so glad you made it home safe. Thanks for doing this."

"I love you, too, Ma."

I fell asleep, and without knowing what happened, my eyes shot open. I was dreaming about the concrete factory in Kirkuk. I was riding in the back of the truck chasing a group of people, all I could see were the backs of their hands as they sprinted away in fear. When we pulled up to them and dismounted to chase them on foot, I ran as hard as I could toward one man until he was within arm's reach and I tackled him. After we wrestled on the ground for a moment, he flipped onto his back and to my god damn surprise, it was my brother. My brother was staring at me, and he had a handgun pointed at my heart and a smirk on his face. Just as he pulled the trigger, I woke up.

My hands were sweaty and my mouth parched. It was pitch black besides the light poles.

"What the fuck," I mumbled repeatedly, "it was only a dream, only a dream." But it seemed so real. You are not in Iraq anymore, you are on a road trip with your mother in Arizona. It's all in the past.

Mother's deep breathing calmed me, reminding me where I was and who I was with. After my breathing slowed, I wiped my forehead and quietly stepped outside to smoke until sunrise.

"How'd you sleep, son?" She asked.

"I slept all right," I said. Not wanting to bring her into my misery and make her worry. "And you?" I opened the trunk, found my toiletries, and brushed my teeth.

"I was out like a light," she said. "I can't even remember falling asleep. I'm looking forward to seeing the Grand Canyon today, it's been too long."

"How long?" I said, toothpaste running down my chin.

"Since our trip with Dan when you were little."

I spat and rinsed my mouth.

"It's time to see it again," I said.

I wanted to tell her about the dream but did not want her to look at me differently. I wanted to tell her about our time at the cement factory but didn't want her to think her son was an aggressive asshole. I wanted to tell her everything, I wanted to tell her nothing. I sure as shit didn't want to sleep anymore, I just wanted to move on with life. So I stepped away from the car and prayed to the pack of smokes to stop my dreams and give me peace. When Mother finished brushing her teeth, we continued north.

"You're quiet this morning, son," she said. "I heard you wake up last night and go outside. What's going on?"

I took a deep breath.

"I could think of a thousand things to talk about," I said, "but there isn't one in particular that stands out. Why what's up with you?"

"Just wondering about my son," she said. "I want to make sure you're all right, and that you don't end up like my daddy."

"Don't worry about me, ma," I said. "I'm good."

"You spent two years over there," she said. "I can tell you did some things."

"It was nothing compared to other guys." I stared out the window at the dark sky wondering how much longer I had in this life.

"My daddy buried his memories with booze," she said. "He couldn't handle them and he couldn't talk about them. Remember, I'm your mother, I remember how you were as a kid. You would hide for hours or days when you were upset or embarrassed. Sometimes you spent an entire week in silence, even when you were called on in school."

"If I need to talk, I'll let you know."

"Okay, son. Just know that I love you. You can always talk to me." She put her hand on my shoulder and I bit my lip.

"I love you, too," I said. "What happened, happened, there is nothing I can do about it."

"You can't change what happened, but you can change how you are affected by it. My daddy didn't smile for years after Vietnam, same with Uncle Smiley. He couldn't even be around his kids anymore because we reminded him of the kids over there. Thank God Uncle Smiley quit drinking, or the same thing would have happened to him; they couldn't talk to anybody for fear of judgment and fear of being weak. I want to make sure you don't take the same route," she said, "that's all. I know how you love to drink, and I want you to be careful."

"Okay, okay," I said. "Jesus Christ, get off my back about it. I didn't see shit over there, nothing like the guys in Vietnam. And I barely drink. Please, stop asking me about it."

Yet I wanted to tell her every story from beginning to end, every detail; the fear, excitement, heartache, and loneliness, but I could not burden her. I wanted to cry in her car as she drove deeper and deeper into the southwest, to leave my darkness in the desert. I wanted her to wrap her arms around me and give me a big motherly hug and tell me that everything is going to be okay and that it was okay to cry. But instead, I lit another cigarette, stuck my head out the window to feel the cold breeze and listen to the wind.

28

We pulled into the Grand Canyon National Park as dozens of buses, vans, and vehicles moved in every direction. When I mentioned it to mother in an aggravated tone, all she said was: "Then let's join the circus," and smiled.

Ever since seeing the Grand Canyon as a child, I have dreamt of hiking to the bottom. To soak my feet in the Colorado River while admiring sky-high red rock walls. It seemed comforting, and I needed comfort. We found a parking space and I turned to mother.

"There is something that I need to do," I said, rubbing my patchy beard.

"I already know, son." She smiled. "You're hiking to the bottom." She laughed. "You act like your own mother doesn't know you."

I nodded and smiled, "You got me."

"Just be safe and make sure to pack plenty of food and water," she said.

"Yes ma'am," I said. "What will you do today?"

"Don't worry about me," she said. "What better place to be?"

I popped the trunk and packed a day bag with three slices of pizza, two peanut butter and jelly sandwiches, four liters of water, a headlamp, a handkerchief, a first aid kit, a camera, trail mix, and granola bars. I swung the bag over my shoulders and gave my mother a hug and kiss.

"I'll be back by sundown," I said. "Let's meet back at the car."

While looking for trail maps and a bus to take me to a prime hiking trail, I noticed multiple signs with advisories that read:

"DO NOT ATTEMPT TO MAKE IT TO THE BOTTOM OF THE CANYON AND BACK IN ONE DAY!"

I could understand during the heat of summer, but in November—Hell, I would be fine.

I loaded a bus and found a seat in the back to keep an eye on the entrance and the canyon rim. Overweight old people with canes, thick sunglasses, and bright pins were the majority; their

styles made me laugh. Everybody in America seemed so big, I thought. Especially after spending time in Italy, other parts of Europe, and the Middle East. The bus riders kept quiet and stayed focused outside, so I did the same. I was drawn to a woman with blonde hair, blue eyes, and acne scars. She was gorgeous and athletic. I quickly imagined sitting on the shore of the Colorado soaking my feet, eating a slice of pizza, when she snuck up behind me and pulled her black tank top over her head tossing it into the river, revealing perfect perky breasts, stomach, ribcage, shoulders, and neck. I touched her soft skin and she touched my bare stomach. I threw the pizza into the river and she unbuckled my belt and kissed my collarbone. I squeezed her hips with both hands and she whispered into my ear, "Take me."

People began to exit. The girl and I got off at the same stop. We made eye contact, smiled and I looked away. I was nervous as hell, so to prevent a conversation from happening, I walked away from her and the bus as fast as possible.

A woman like that would never like a murderer like me, I thought.

I checked the time on my phone and it was later than I hoped, just after ten. I smoked on the rim, admiring separate layers of red running down the walls. It was my first time hiking into a canyon and I didn't know how to approach it. The bottom didn't look very far away. I asked God to watch over me, tightened the shoulder straps, and hit the trail. A fast walk became a slow trot. And even though I didn't feel like I was moving fast, people cheered like I was a hero as I passed them.

Maybe the countless hours spent filling sandbags were training for this moment. Maybe I was punishing myself for terrifying thousands of people in the middle of the night. Maybe I was running away from my longing for my father and brother, both of whom didn't seem to give a damn about the youngest Stark. I started sprinting down the trail, leaving the rim far behind. I stopped after a bit to hydrate and observe, but I don't remember seeing anything but red rocks; red everywhere, inside and outside. Where is that lovely woman? I wondered. I looked up the trail and noticed people no larger than ants. I jogged and jogged and jogged until a metal bridge passed over the Colorado River, where I sat down and hung my legs and smoked as muscle spasms shook my body.

"This is a good place to die," I said, looking into the water below. "I wish the water could cleanse my conscience."

I drank water and then struggled to my feet to follow the path to a small beach along the river. I dropped the pack to stretch, hydrate, and eat. My feet and legs hurt. I took off my shoes to soak my blistered feet in the river, finished the water, and stretched some more. I watched and listened for wildlife but saw none. It was deafeningly quiet. I hoped the blonde girl would appear. Fluffy clouds floated across the sky and obscured the sun. I ate the pizza, and halfway through the third slice, I thought it would be wise to save some, but I was so damn hungry I couldn't stop. I ate both sandwiches, too, saving the granola bars and trail mix for the hike up. I decided to search for a potable water station and found a narrow path crossing a stream through a grove. It felt cool and relaxing, like the mossy control room at the water treatment facility. I continued walking and found a restroom and watering station, so I filled the bottles, returned to my pack, and decided to lie on the shore with my feet elevated on a boulder. Without realizing it, I fell asleep, and I woke up to a soft female voice saying, "Wake up, Robert, wake up."

I scrambled for a second, looked at my watch, and realized it was much later than I wanted. So I packed my stuff and began lacing my shoes. I could've sworn I noticed movement on the metal bridge and when I looked up it was the blonde woman from the bus. But what the heck do I know, I was exhausted, dreamy, and alone.

"Hey," I said. "Wait up."

I put on my pack to follow. The sun had begun its descent, and I had no idea how long it would take to hike out. My legs and feet shot through with pain. I crossed the bridge and noticed different shades of red from earlier. Had things become lighter or darker? The blonde woman was gone, she must've just been a figment of my imagination.

I trudged the switchbacks with shaky hands, achy feet, and a huge smile, repeating the mantra, "This is the pattern, this is the way. Steadily upward, I'll make it today."

I remembered a friend of my mother's, Marie Smith Jones, the last Eyak to speak her language who had recently passed away. We used to visit her home in Anchorage when I was a boy and she would sit inside and chain smoke Marlboro 100s with long bony fingers. She was so small we had to be gentle when hugging her. Mother said that Marie had a direct link to the spirit world, an ability to communicate with those who had passed, and those who had not yet been born. I stopped to smoke in her honor, wondering where did her spirit go? Did she truly have contact with spirits? Is there a life after death, and if so, what is it like?

There was movement in the corner of my eye, and I swear

on the medals I earned in Iraq that the blonde woman was way up the trail looking back at me like she was waiting. I waved, there was no return wave. I was speechless, kind of afraid, and curious. She continued staring down the trail at me, so I finished my cigarette and started trudging upward.

I wish I could give a long, beautiful, lyrical description of the feelings that were going on inside me at the time, or of the vivid colors and natural beauty of the area, but, I was so lost in physical and mental pain that I could not see or feel anything, let alone describe it.

I continued walking while staring at the ground, willing my feet to move. Up, and up, and up. After a solid leg, I stopped to break and could swear on my Subaru station wagon that the girl was closer than before like I had gained on her, and she raised her right arm and pointed at the sky.

I looked up at the rising moon and setting sun, realizing that it would be dark soon.

"I see you're the type who likes to hike alone," I yelled. "That's cool, me too."

A gust of wind blew sand in my eyes, so I lowered my head to keep walking.

"What the fuck is going on here?" I whispered.

And when I lifted my head, the girl was gone. Maybe she sprinted ahead, went around a bend, or ducked behind a boulder, I thought. Hell, maybe she's just a figure of my imagination.

"Only a little further," I said. "You got this."

Knowing that I didn't want to be hiking in the dark,

I pushed it hard. My feet were in more pain than during any road march I'd done in the military. I looked up at the smiling moon and setting sun, and thought: It's not so bad to be alive. I could've sworn that I saw the woman's silhouette so far up the trail it seemed impossible. Perhaps she was an ultramarathoner? I remembered the daydream on the bus and thought that maybe if I made it to the top of the rim fast enough she would still be there and we could make the dream come true. So I pushed hard the rest of the way, slowly walking upward until reaching the rim.

At the rim, I dropped the nearly empty pack, lit a smoke, and stared into the dark abyss. The woman was nowhere to be seen. I suddenly wondered if angels were real and thought that maybe she was an angel sent to help me?

I caught the next, and final, bus to the visitor's center. I looked in the side mirror of the Pontiac and noticed a glimmering light in my eyes that was not there before. I scratched my beard, smiled, and plopped on the pavement with my back resting on a tire and legs stretched out. My phone was dead. People walked by and said, "Hello" and I said it back. Children stared in wonder and amazement. I lay on the concrete using my backpack as a pillow and fell asleep.

I awoke to my mother standing over me with a sandwich and a smile.

"You look tired, son." She laughed. "I was beginning to worry. Are you hungry?"

"You have no idea," I said.

I struggled to stand and she hugged me and then handed

me the sandwich. I devoured it on our way to a restaurant. After dinner, we found a rest area, and I stretched out in the back and slept harder than I had in years.

"Hey, Robert... Robert, it's time to wake up..."

The familiar sound of my mother's voice brought comfort, and a reminder of elementary school when she would wake me up and then I'd eat cereal while she smoked by the open door. That was before she quit, before she died of lung cancer, after this road trip.

I stepped outside the car to smoke as my tight muscles screamed. My entire body was in such excruciating pain I could hardly move. I shuffled to the wood line to pee, brushed my teeth, then watched the sunrise beside Mother. I felt okay. We spat toothpaste in the grass together and rinsed our mouths with the same bottle of water. It felt good to share with her; I had missed her so much. I wanted to tell her how much, and how thankful I was for the care packages, but I was afraid that I would start crying and I needed to be strong so I didn't say a thing.

"I'll be driving again today, thank you very much," she said, smiling.

"I don't think I could if I wanted," I said. "My legs are killing me."

"That's what I figured," she said. "We'll have a long day of cruising."

We traveled north on Highway 89 under a clear blue sky as rocky, dry landscapes flashed by. Hello Utah, goodbye Utah. I was hoping to see a band of polygamists dancing naked on the roadside and was disappointed when I saw none. My expectations are usually unrealistic. We listened to a new Cat Stevens album under the name of Yusuf Islam; his voice and message soothed me. Then we listened to mother's favorites: Alicia Keys, Motown Collections, Matchbox Twenty, Bob Seger, Patsy Cline, Marvin Gaye, The Judds, and Johnny Cash. We did a map check and turned off 89 onto 9 to skirt around the south end of Zion National Park.

During my second deployment, I had a 3-ring binder with motivating magazine clippings in plastic sheets. Reminders that my deployment and time in the Army were almost over, and I would soon have free will to do whatever I wanted. Pictures of hiking trails and national parks, camping tips and gear guides, long-haired men with beards who appeared easy-going and pretty women with white teeth and no makeup, exotic travel destinations, and snowy mountains that I hoped to visit. A picture of Henry Rollins with his shirt off yelling into a microphone and Arnold as a young man doing curls;

Jessica Alba with a slight smile in a bikini, and Jessica Biel…
the beautiful Jessica Biel. Two pages were dedicated to Zion
National Park.

We cruised through Rockville, Springdale, and Virgin.

"Maybe I'll buy a cabin here," I said. "And marry a virgin."

Mother laughed and shook her head.

None of the towns grabbed our attention enough to stop,
and before we knew it we were passing the park entrance. I
lightly nudged her with an elbow. "What do you think?" I
said, pointing at a gorgeous red rock arch in the near distance.
"We going in?"

She shrugged and rubbed the palm of her left hand with
her fingertips.

"It's up to you, son," she said. "With you being as sore as
you are, I think the best thing we can do is take it easy and
cover some ground."

I smiled in relief.

"Thank you," I said. "I would love to come back here to
explore and camp for a couple of weeks, just not today."

"You will, son," she said. "When you put your mind to
something, there's no stopping you. Do you need to stop for
anything?"

"No ma'am," I said.

"Then, let's cruise." She smiled, turned up the music, and
sang along with Patsy Cline.

I turned my head and bit my lip. I hadn't realized how
much I missed her until being with her again. It was like
being in a desert for months without rain until a squall hits

and standing outside with your shirt off and eyes closed, arms raised to the sky, you realize how badly you had missed the rain.

We stopped at a diner and ordered two black coffees and two typical American breakfasts; two eggs over medium, sausage or bacon, hash-browns, and toast. I replaced the meat with an additional egg. Mother smiled and said, "Good morning" to everybody, everybody said it back. An old couple with thin gray hair and matching sweaters ate in a booth beside us. They didn't talk to each other the entire time. A family of six large and loud people made a mess at a round table; two big boys, two big girls, and two big parents with food splattered on all of their big faces. Scrambled eggs were pressed into the carpet under them. It was disgusting and disrespectful, so I turned my attention to the dreamcatchers and pictures of Zion hanging on the walls. The waitress paced with a pot of coffee and a lipstick frown; I paid and we filled the tank then hit the road.

Mother set the cruise control at seventy-five, and the miles flew by. She kicked back and sucked on hard candies, driving with one hand and singing to the music. I wondered what she was thinking about?

About her husband and their situation? She didn't care that her family disapproved, and I respected her for that. While they believed in Jesus Christ and studied his teachings on forgiveness, she forgave and refused to judge people on their mistakes. He makes her feel beautiful, special, appreciated; a lot different from Dan. Will he ever get out? Twenty-five years for killing somebody seems long enough, especially because soldiers are paid to do it. Was she thinking about James in Juneau? How much pain he had caused her over the years? How no matter what she had done to try and set James on the right track he always found a way to use drugs and alcohol and get into some kind of trouble. Was she worried about visiting family in Idaho?

I will never know what she was thinking, just like she will never know what was on my mind because we were raised to keep our thoughts to ourselves and have no idea how to express any emotion other than anger, sadness, and happiness. Consequentially, the majority of the time we spent together as mother and son was in silence. I love silence.

"You going to keep me company or what?" she said. I woke up with warm sunlight beaming through the window on my face. I turned to see her smiling eyes. My body was tight and painful, my heart was at ease.

"Sorry, Mom," I said. "I'm just tired."

"I'll bet you are," she said. "You've been sleeping for three hours."

"Wow," I said, sitting upright. "That's crazy."

"I don't know if I can handle family for more than a couple of days," she said.

"We don't have to," I said, surprised that she would share a thought like that with me. "Let's get in, say hello, and get out."

"Ever since I married Victor…well…things changed," she said. "I can't help my feelings for him, and I don't want confrontation."

"It will be okay," I said. "If they talk shit, I'll tell them to mind their own business."

She laughed, "Thanks, son. That's why I wanted boys, to take care of their mama. Why do families get away with treating each other so poorly?" She asked.

"Maybe because we take each other for granted until we're not around anymore," I said. "Maybe they don't understand how you can be so happily married to a man doing life in prison while people with millions of dollars are miserable. People with lots of things don't like seeing people without lots of things happy, it doesn't make sense, and then it makes them look at themselves."

"People and stuff come and go," she said. "It's what's right here that matters." She touched her heart. "Do you remember Marie?"

"Of course," I said. "I'll never forget her."

"I was with her twice when she talked with spirits. Of course, I didn't hear any voices, but I could sure as heck feel their presence. Our bodies turn to ash, Robert, but our spirits live on. What matters in life is not how much money we spend but how much quality time we spend with each other."

I looked at her in amazement. She did not use to speak so philosophically, or maybe I did not listen. She had sure changed in the four-plus years I was away in the Army.

"Well, Ma," I said, placing my hand on her shoulder. "If it means anything, as long as you are happy—I am happy. I got your back, no matter what."

"I know you do, son." She smiled. "Sometimes I need to hear it, though," she said. "I think we all do."

We arrived in Jackson Hole long after dark. I had heard about the ski resort my entire life and was disappointed that the fog was too thick to see the mountain. The only restaurant open was Denny's. I love Denny's. Two employees spoke Spanish in the parking lot, and I wished I could understand. Mother said hello and they returned the greeting. We ate and left. It was quick and uneventful; not delicious or disgusting, not great service or terrible, but always the same and always open. It did the trick. We left the blinding lights of condominiums and pulled off the road a dozen miles from Yellowstone, where an artificial light could not be seen. The glow of the moon was beautiful; I wondered if Elliot was admiring the same moon reflecting from the Pacific Ocean while thinking of me.

I reclined the seat back and within minutes mother was breathing heavily in the back. I found her rhythm and drifted away until I awoke covered in sweat with my heart thumping. I was sprinting after the rifle I had dropped in the sand, terrified that the locals would get to it before me and kill me and my comrades with my rifle. I wanted to yell but could not. I went outside to smoke and listen to the wind. I grabbed at the present moment but kept drifting to the past. I quietly opened the door and the glove box to grab my headlamp, journal, and the pen the lady gave me in Kentucky. I followed a narrow footpath to a small body of water and sat on a log to write as tears streamed down my face.

You kill a man to set him free.
Is this the man I want to be?
Look in my eyes, now do you see,
What this war has done to me?
Why do I feel the things I feel?
Why me Lord, do I have to kill?
I do not believe, I do not agree,
But what can I do, they'll punish me?
I've done my time here, please let me go,
I beg and I beg, but you keep saying no.
Why do this to us? Our country disagrees,
We write and we call, you ignore all our pleas.
We are all scared, we don't want to die.
For no rhyme, no reason,
Can you tell me why?
At first, I was proud, saying: "Mommy, look at me,
I'm all grown up, be proud, you'll see.
I will fight, I will bleed, I could possibly die,
But mother, don't worry, the terrorists, that's why.
The Man called us up, now we have to go,
I'm sorry mother, you couldn't know."
"Pack your bags let's go, we're off to war!"
An 18-year-old kid can't imagine the horror.
'Here we go,' I thought. 'Let's do this right,
Let's kill those bastards in the middle of the night.'
The protesting I watched on the PX TV,
Why would they do this?
I was too blind to see.

I was a madman at first, ready to kill,
'Everyone's a suspect,' I thrived on the thrill.
I saw murder and suffering, forced to watch some folk die,
Hardass grown men on their knees crying: "Why?"
We boys became men in a matter of days,
Innocence vanished, only left with a trace.
Windshields do shatter and people do scream,
Sometimes I wonder, 'Was it just a bad dream?'
They sent us boys home for just a short break,
Families were torn, smiles were fake.
Children were crying while daddies stood strong,
Wives felt damn guilty, many hearts were long gone.
Now the war is over but the nightmares stay true,
Waking up sweating, "Just me? No, you too?"
Your son lost nearly everything in that horrible place,
Innocence vanished, only left with a trace.
We thought we were finished, the Man had different plans,
We are modern-day pirates conquering foreign lands.
Now, I am back here again, Ma, this time not the same,
Why the hell are we here? They seem to think it's a game.
Kids are still dying, please tell me why,
End this damn violence, there is no reason to die.
I speak for the many, we do not agree,
Please give us the reason, it matters to me.
If I die right now, I will die in shame,
Fighting for what, who the hell is to blame?
But no, the stop-loss is here,
they won't let me move on.

I did my four years,
Is there something wrong?
I bled, I killed,
I fought and I cried,
Please let me go home, tell my Mom that I tried.

I went back to the car and fell asleep, waking up some time later to my mother quietly opening the trunk. I watched her walk down the same trail with her camera and return thirty minutes or so later. She brushed her teeth beside the car and then took more pictures of sun rays streaming through the fog. She held her breath for a delicate moment, lightly pressing the shutter like a finger on a trigger, then released her breath as fog on a cold morning. Ever since I can remember, when people have asked her how she is doing, she says the same thing. "I woke up this morning with a roof over my head, food on the table, and love in my heart. What more can I ask for?"

As I achingly stepped into the cool morning air, mother insisted on a hug.

"How did you sleep, son?"

"All right," I said. "You?"

"Like I was back on daddy's lap as a little girl," she said. "You care to talk about your dreams?" I was surprised by her question. "I heard you tossing and turning again last night, and then you got out of the car."

"It's nothing," I said. "I just needed to smoke."

"If you ever want to talk," she said. "I'm all ears."

"I will let you know, thanks."

Where the hell would I begin? I thought. What am I supposed to say?

'Well, ma, I launched a bunch of grenades at people, and one time I blew up a white Toyota with red letters and killed two guys. I probably killed others, too, but I don't know for sure. I only did it to keep from dying, and to keep my buddies from dying, but it still haunts me. Is it against nature to kill one's species? Who is to say how many women and children I woke up with a rifle in their face, shouting in a foreign language to get in the yard to be separated and questioned. I tore through their dressers! How would I feel if somebody came and ripped all the clothes out of my dresser and threw them on the floor? Especially if they were clean! I stomped dirt all over their rugs and searched underneath, they were real nice rugs, too, Ma, you would have loved them. I remember what you always said about karma, Ma… So what will come from my exploits? Because I feel guilty even thinking about them.'

Why do I only recall negative memories from Iraq? I'm sure I could find some positive ones to share. Instead, I walked away from the car to brush my teeth in the fog. Where it was quiet and peaceful and black and white did not exist. I need to find a way to live with these memories or I will live in misery, I thought.

I went back to the car where my mother was in the driver's seat smiling.

"You're driving again, I take it?"

"Is that okay?" She rubbed her hands together.

"Of course," I said, "but please don't hesitate to ask if you want to switch. I feel a lot better today." She nodded and started the engine. "I watched you brushing this morning."

"You were watching me?" she said, laughing. "You've always been so sneaky."

"It has done me well," I said. "You seem to be at peace, Ma. It is great to see."

"I could get used to not working forty to sixty hours a week." She laughed. "And like I said, this is my first unplanned trip since I was a little girl, and it feels empowering to rough it like this, so there isn't a reason in the world not to be at peace... ya know, son?"

We pulled into Yellowstone and paid a bearded ranger who looked like the long-haired, happy-go-lucky men in the three-ring binder. We followed a windy road to a sign for Old Faithful and pulled into a nearly empty parking lot. We noticed a sign with predicted eruption times at the tourist center and since we only had twenty minutes, we decided to go outside and sit on a bench to wait. Many people had fancy cameras on tripods. There was a group of happy-looking Asian girls flashing peace signs and smiling for the camera. An old gray-haired man pushed an old gray-haired lady in a wheelchair past a leathery woman with a dyed blonde perm who was alone on a bench.

"Look at the diversity, son," said mother. "People from all around the world came to see the beauty and power of Mother Earth. It reminds me of being in Seward, doesn't it?"

"Yeah it does," I said. "That's what I loved the most about

the military, the diversity. All I knew about other cultures before was from the movies."

"What about your stepfather and his family?" She said. "You can't forget Grandpa, Sharice, Latoya, and the kids. Remember when grandpa moved into your room and you skipped school to spend time with him?" She laughed. "He loved you so much."

"I skipped school because he would fall asleep watching Judge Judy, and I would roll a bunch of his cigarettes out of his can." "He didn't mind," she said. "He knew what you were doing. We talked about it."

"Really?" I said.

"Of course son," she said. "He wasn't dumb. He was usually just resting his eyes. And, I am your mother; I know a lot more than you think."

"So maybe I had some multicultural experience," I said, "but not much. I'll never forget, all Grandpa ate was sandwiches with a fried hot dog, cheesy scrambled eggs, and jam."

She laughed, "They are delicious."

She pulled back her jacket sleeve to check the time on a Mickey Mouse watch.

"Three minutes," she said.

Less than thirty seconds later the geyser began to burp and dry-heave until BAM! scalding hot liquid shot fifty feet in the air. Time froze. People scurried about trying to take a perfect picture. We stood still. My mother left her camera in the car on purpose, she did not want to miss the moment. It wasn't long before Old Faithful came to a sputtering halt, and the old woman in the wheelchair yelled at the man pushing her toward the parking lot, "Okay Harry, check it off the bucket list!" The entire crowd moved in the same direction, us included.

On the Yellowstone Highway, drivers tailed our bumper on narrow windy roads and then slammed their brakes to pull off for photographs. Thankfully, the weather was clear and the roads dry. We stopped to watch bison graze beside a steamy river, listen to a strange growl from behind a waterfall, wonder how bugs survive the heat and smell of various colored geothermic pools, and use the restroom. We went sight to sight until five o'clock when we decided to hit the exit and head west toward Caldwell.

The freeway was packed, semis went by going twenty over the speed limit. Mother flashed her lights when they had enough room to merge, they flashed their brake lights to thank her.

"I learned that from my daddy," she said. "It's a kind gesture. Truckers have it hard."

We were blinded by the sunset over flat, golden farmland.

I wondered what would life be like if I had stayed living in Idaho as a child and never gone to Alaska?

When we passed Nampa, I called grandma for directions. She was living in an extra room with my aunt and her new husband.

"Grandma," I said. "It's Robert, Sheri's son."

"I'll be god damned," she yelled. "You little shit. How the

fuck are ya? I hear you're coming to visit your ol' grandma. It's about damn time!"

"Yes ma'am," I said laughing. "We're pulling into Caldwell now and need directions."

"Your mama said ya'll was coming out here to see your grandma. It's about god damn time," she coughed into the phone and mumbled, "Jesus fucking christ." She gave directions between coughs, curses, and sniffles.

"All right Grandma," I said. "We'll see you in a few."

"It's sure gonna be good to see you two," she said. "I love the fuckin' shit out of you guys!"

"We love you, too, Grandma." Mother and I laughed as I hung up the phone.

Mother turned on a dark street in a dark neighborhood in the same town where she delivered two sons and lived for years. Grandma was standing in the middle of the street wearing a robe and slippers, she was wiping her nose on a folded paper towel she carried in a gloved hand—the other hand had a drink and a cigarette. She flipped us off, smiled, then pointed at the house. We pulled into the driveway.

"I'll be god damned," she said, knocking on the driver's side door. "Get out here and give your mama a hug!" We hugged her and kissed her on the lips. "You grew into a decent-looking young man," she said, "you little shit!"

"Thanks, Grandma," I said. "It's nice to see you, too."

She led us inside. "I'm glad to see you're alive," she said. "I was worried about ya, fighting them rag heads and all." I winced at the word. I was surprised; I didn't think she knew

I existed. "Last time I saw you, you were just a tiny Idaho potato. Now look at you, you're a grown man." My mother could not stop giggling.

"It's been a long time, Grandma," I said. "You probably didn't realize, but as time progresses people grow up."

"Well, no shit Sherlock," she said, laughing. "I raised six God-Damn-Little-Shits before you were born, so don't go tryin' to tell me about raisin' kids. You little shit! You probably don't know your asshole from your elbow, do ya?"

"I know that I can wipe my asshole with my elbow," I said. "I do yoga."

"You must be a flexible son-of-a-bitch," she said. We laughed and found a seat on a couch. "Ya'll want a beer?" she said.

"Does a whale live underwater?" I said.

"You tell me, Mr. Alaska," she said. "I don't know a god damn thing about whales."

"I would love a beer," said mother.

"Well, then go outside and get yourselves one," she said. "They're on the back deck, grab one for me, too, while you're at it."

I walked through the kitchen out the back door and found a half-empty twenty-four pack of Natural Ice Light on the deck. Five dogs in a small chain link fence wanted to rip my throat out.

"Shut up," I heard Grandma yell from inside. "Those dogs drive me nuts," said grandma, when I handed her the beer. "Remember when I went to visit you in Nome, Sheri."

Mother nodded. "What's the first thing I did up there?" We laughed, shrugged, and shook our heads. "You kiddies don't have to play dumb with me, you know damn good and well I went straight to the bar to teach those old boys a lesson." She laughed at the memory. "They could hardly believe that I was a real person. Those people in Alaska loved the shit out of me!" She coughed into the paper towel and wiped her lips. "They didn't know what hit 'em when Ol' Shirley Anne came through. Ha! Because I tell it how it is! And, I'll tell you what, by the time I left Alaska, those ol' boys loved the shit out of me. God damn, I love Alaska!"

I laughed so hard my sides hurt.

"Why did they love you so much, Grandma?" I egged her on.

"Because your Grandma tells it how it is," she said. "I don't church myself up for nobody, I don't give a damn who ya' are!" she smiled, revealing a few missing teeth. "I remember when you kids were children," she looked at mother, "I had you little shits trained. Didn't I, Sheri? Didn't I?"

"You sure did," mother said, with tears on her cheeks from laughing.

"You knew not to say a damn thing before I finished a pot of coffee," she said. "You kids would be as still as a painting, without a damn sound. 'Cause you knew damn well that before I had my first pot, I was a mean bitch. Ha! That time of day is reserved for silence. Ain't that right, Sheri?"

"Darn rights," said mother. "We were scared to death of you."

Grandma laughed hysterically and leaned back in the recliner. Her magnified brown eyes blinked behind thick glasses, her mouth slightly open like she could hardly hold back her thoughts.

"Children are supposed to fear their parents," she said. "Otherwise, they go bat shit crazy. Kids had discipline in those days. I would go to the grocery store with six kids, each one holding the shopping cart, not touching a god damn thing." She laughed. "People asked how I did it and I didn't know, I just done it the way my mama did. Hell, nowadays, kids walk all over their parents and then expect to do the same to everybody else. Not my kids, you kids became hard-working members of society."

"Today's parents were whipped by their daddies for no good reason," said mother. "They want no part in the violence."

"Oh, hell Sheri," said grandma, shaking her head. "I hope you didn't raise your boys like that."

"I'm not saying parents nowadays are right," said mother. "It's that parenting styles differ from families and generations. What worked for my generation might not work for Robert's."

I looked at mother in awe; she had changed so much since I left. It seemed that the phone calls, letters, and visits made her articulate, thoughtful, and courageous with her words.

"Kids will be kids no matter what generation," said grandma. "You were always the smartest of the kids, Sheri. Look at your sharp brain, now." Mother blushed. "You wouldn't have turned out that way if I pampered you. But you're right." Grandma nodded. "You're right, the times are changing and it's important to change with them. Otherwise, you'll be stuck in the past just like your daddy was. And that'll kill ya. You two want to step out for a smoke?"

"I could use a smoke," I said, still baffled by my mother's brave words.

"I quit smoking ten years ago," said mother.

"I'll be god damned," said grandma. "Good girl, well, that means there are more cigarettes for us then, thank you very much."

The two of us went on the deck and the dogs erupted.

"Shut up!" Grandma whacked the fence three times with her cane and the dogs stopped barking and curled up in the corner. I opened another beer and listened to Grandma talk about how awful the poor dogs were treated, being forced to stay in that small cage with a handful of strangers for weeks on end. "I'd be barking too!" She said.

When we went inside, mother had returned from grabbing our toiletries from outside and was smiling on the couch.

"Put a pitchfork in this old bitch," said Grandma, standing in the doorway to her room. "I'm fucking done. I'll see you kids tomorrow."

We gave her hugs and kisses before she disappeared into her room to speak softly to her pet chihuahua named Tinkerbell. Mother and I brushed our teeth in the bathroom, where two books by Ted Nugent were on the back of the toilet, then giggled while making our beds. She removed her glasses, said goodnight, and rolled over. I turned off the lamp and tried to fall asleep but could not. So I crept out the front door to smoke, think, and breathe Caldwell air.

There was no better treat as a kid than talking to grandma on the phone. Any time we answered, mother knew it was grandma because we laughed so hard. James and I would sit on the floor with our ears pressed together laughing. The first thing grandma always said, was: "How the fuck have you little shits been doing?" Mother would shake her head, smile, and say: "It must be your Grandmother."

She drank her beer in an iced mug with ice cubes. She put the mug in the freezer before bed with about a quarter glass of beer in the bottom and then filled it around noon the following day. She spent her days watching TV shows, always rooting for the cop to catch the bad guy. She loved John Wayne, Chuck Norris, and Charlie Pride. She talked, laughed, cried, and cursed at the screen. She loved the shit out of Tinkerbell, she would say it all the time. She also loved her collection of dreamcatchers, Native American blankets, trinkets, and artwork. It didn't matter if they were bought at a gas station and made in China. She took great pride in her Seminole blood, and often said, "We were the last ones to sign the fucking peace treaty! We are warriors on all sides!" Whether any of this was true or not, I have not verified, but she loved to say it. She repeated stories about meeting people in bars who loved the shit out of her. "I'll tell you why because I tell it how it is. I don't church up nothing for nobody; I don't give two shits who ya are, I am who I am and if you don't like it, go fuck a duck!" She would wipe her mouth with a paper towel she always kept in her gloved hand.

Her first husband, my grandfather Donald Raymond Moore Sr., died from cirrhosis at forty-three. She remarried years later and her second husband, Arturo Hernandez, died in his sixties and left her alone in a state of dependency, although she would say otherwise. I met him once, he was painting a portrait of grandma in a tank top and shorts sitting on a porch swing smoking a long, skinny cigarette and drinking a beer. He was a tall, thin Native American/ Mexican man. Tolerant, quiet, and kind. He would have to be to deal with grandma for thirty years.

It was hard for me to believe that I was back in Caldwell, Idaho. Back with my grandmother and mother. Back from Iraq in a safe house with a family who cared about me. I couldn't identify the feelings inside me, whether I felt good or bad, whether I felt happy or sad, whether I felt anything at all. But after six cigarettes, I was finally tired, so I went back inside to curl up on the couch and rest.

31

I surprised grandma the next morning while mother was making breakfast.

"You're a what," she said, looking at me like I was a crazy person. "A vegetarian…what the hell is that?"

I laughed and gave her a quick rundown.

"I'm not against people eating meat," I said, "but I am against the maltreatment of animals. I don't think any living being should be treated the way factory-farmed animals are. And I don't want to support that industry."

"Well, fuck a duck!" she said, shrugging and blinking. "You can eat whatever the hell you want and I'll eat whatever the hell I want, thank you very much."

I smiled and salted the potatoes.

"I appreciate the support, grandma," I said.

"No problemo." She snickered and put a heavy hand on my hip. "Now get the fuck out of the way so I can smoke."

I laughed and stepped aside. Mother and I made eye contact and smiled.

If only the rest of the world was as accepting as grandma, I thought. When I became a vegetarian just before my twenty-first birthday, some of the guys I served with asked questions like, "Are you a faggot or something, Stark?" They were always trying to have seething debates about the benefits of meat, about the fact that we had teeth that were made to eat meat, and that it even says in the Bible that animals were put on Earth to be eaten by humans. I didn't engage in these debates, the only thing that mattered to me was that by choosing not to eat animals my damaged heart felt better every meal. And after my first tour, which was quickly followed by a divorce, I needed any help I could get to feel better about myself.

After grandma finished smoking, we ate breakfast at a table covered in NRA magazines.

We invited Grandma to come with us to visit her brother, my Great Uncle Smiley, and his wife, Aunt Anita, but she refused. So we drove across town to the two-acre parcel they once farmed and shared with Great Grandma Fanny, whom I visited twice in my life. I carried fond memories of stretching taffy, watching the Cubs, and exploring the storm cellar.

I was a little nervous to visit Uncle Smiley. He was a loud, opinionated, judgmental man who had retired from the army as a chief warrant officer and treated everybody as a new recruit. He had expressed his disapproval of my mother's newest marriage by yelling at her on the phone and disowning her. Mother continued to call and talk with Aunt

Anita, but he refused to speak with her. Mother later mailed them a Seward Journal Newspaper with an anti-war poem I had published during my second tour, and he disowned me. Even after we had such a great time together two years prior when I visited them while on leave between duty stations. I didn't understand why she had sent the damn poem to everybody in the family, especially because we live in a very American, right-wing, military family and the poem was anti-colonialism. When I asked her why she sent it to everybody she smiled and said: "Because it was an awesome poem."

When we arrived at their pretty white corner lot house, Smiley stood on the porch with a frown while Aunt Anita came downstairs to hug us at the door. Mother hugged Smiley and he kept his arms by his sides and stared forward.

He turned to me and said, "Why would you write such a god-awful poem? You were on orders and you betrayed your country."

Aunt Anita stepped between us and said, "Let's go inside, dear. I made lunch."

Mother followed her through a screen door and Smiley blocked my entrance.

"You took an oath to stand by your Commander in Chief no matter what," he said. "Then you betray him. How dare you, you coward; you should be locked away for treason."

I shook my head. "Maybe we took different oaths," I said. "I signed up to serve a free country. Where a person can freely state their opinion. What country did you serve?"

His fat face turned beet red.

"You little dimwit," he said. "You don't know the first thing about service."

"I'm not sure how it was in Vietnam," I said, "but many of us in Iraq didn't see our purpose, so I had to say something."

His narrow eyes filled with rage, and I thought he was going to try and fight me.

"You were not trained to listen to your damn feelings," he said. "Nobody gives a damn about your feelings. When you sign the dotted line and salute the Commander in Chief, you sign your life away, and you learn to keep your damn mouth shut! Do you understand me, boy?"

"I understand your opinion," I said, "but it doesn't mean I agree. I think…"

"You were a god damn specialist," he said. "I was a warrant officer! You were not paid to think, I was. Get it in your thick head, you volunteered—you were not drafted—you can share your experience with civilians but nobody will understand. Nobody cares. They will only judge you as they judged us. None of your drinking buddies in Alaska, or your lovely ex-wife, gives a damn about what you saw; lock it in the armory and forget about it." He took a deep breath, pulled out an orange bottle from his pocket, and popped a couple of pills.

"I will not be another war vet who numbs himself with a bottle of pills," I said. "Nor will I stand in the corner with my mouth shut."

He slammed his thick chest against me.

"Do not disrespect me on my porch," he said. "In front of my family!"

Aunt Anita swung open the door and said, "Okay, boys, it's time to eat."

"One second, love," he said. "We are almost through here."

"Almost," she replied, touching his shoulder. "Give Bobby Joe a break, he just got back from Iraq. Forgive him, darling, he is what they call 'open-minded.'"

"I don't give a damn what he is," he said. "He's a criminal in my mind."

"Only we can describe what happens during combat," I said. "We have a duty to tell people. To do whatever we can to stop the killing of innocent people."

"It's war, boy!" he slammed his fist against the siding. "It has always happened and will always happen. Chickens brood, dogs eat shit and men kill each other, just like leaves fall in autumn."

"I don't see it like that," I said. "And please, back up." I moved a couple of steps back. "I can't accept that," I said. "People can be taught to love differences instead of fear them."

"Boys, let's go inside," said Aunt Anita, calmly. "Lunch is getting cold."

"Who the hell are you, anyway?" he said. "Just some dimwit, bullet catcher who couldn't hack it in the infantry. I burned your stupid poem. You oughta quit writing before you start, you're no good at it." He walked past his wife inside.

We sat down at the table to eat bologna sandwiches with chips and cheese dip.

"The poem caused quite a stir in Seward," said mother. "Dozens of people came up to me at the store to tell me how impressed they were by Robert's writing. It opened their hearts."

"What, are there two thousand people in Seward?" he said. "What kind of change will that make?"

"Three thousand," I said.

"It should be against the law to publish crap like that," he said. "You are a traitor."

"You sound like Big Brother from 1984," I said. "I thought this was a democracy."

"What the hell are you talking about, boy?" he said. "You should be in a cell with your sick brother."

"Smiley!" said Aunt Anita, slamming her hand on the table. "Quiet! Now…"

I smiled, my written words struck a note. The poem was a success.

I finished my meal and stood up to examine a wall of framed photographs of family members who had served in the military. They were shaped in a triangle based on generation, with my great grandfather at the top. My picture was on the bottom next to a couple of cousins I hardly knew. I was surprised it was still up. When Smiley finished eating, he put honey in his tea, folded a paper towel in his hand, and went downstairs to the basement. That was the end of our visit.

That night, our family gathered for a barbecue at Uncle Joe and Aunt Teresa's home in Meridian. Every family member in the area came except for the aunt and her new husband who were out of town. Grandma, Uncle Smiley, Aunt Anita, cousin Danielle, and her son Chase came with her new boyfriend who recently had an operation to remove fat and shrink his stomach, and Aunt Teresa's mother stayed in her room quilting. The grill seared meat and the oven-roasted potatoes. Laughter flowed like soda and beer, a football game was on TV. Grandma had advised her little brother to keep his trap shut and he did. I stayed in the backyard smoking with Uncle Joe while he ran the grill and talked about his son in Iraq.

Uncle Joe is a retired sergeant major turned corrections officer. He did twenty-six years in the army without any combat tours. The lucky guy. He is straightforward, caring, and kind. He met Teresa when he was 19 in Germany, two weeks away from being transferred. He was drinking too much, at the time, as we all do, and he asked her to marry him and come to the states. She agreed, with a strict stipulation that he quit drinking. They have been married ever since, and they swear to God they have never fought.

"I learned one thing in my thirty-one years of marriage," he said. "I learned how to always get the last word." I looked at him confused, it didn't seem like him. He smiled and continued, "No matter what kind of discussion or argument we have, I always end it by saying, 'Yes ma'am.'"

Despite his kindness, especially after the dealings with Smiley, I was ready to be ambushed on all sides.

"Rumor has it that you're a vegetarian," he said, with a smile on his face and tongs in his hand. He licked barbecue sauce from his finger. "What's that all about?"

"It's true," I said. "I don't eat meat."

"It just tastes so good," he said. "Why not?"

"After my first tour," I said. "My heart hurt. So I decided I would do something to try and feel better. I figured, if I can be kind to animals, maybe I can be kind to humans."

"I think it's a bit weird," he said. "Only because I don't know what the hell you would eat." He put his hand on my shoulder. "But don't worry about it, nephew, I love you, no matter what."

I lowered my head. "Thank you," I said. "Thank you so much."

"It just means there's more chicken for me, that's all," he said laughing. He flipped the drumsticks and breasts, juice dripped on the flame and crackled. "You're the one missing out, not me."

Aunt Teresa stepped out to smoke and tell me how happy she was that I made it home.

"I was so worried," she said. "I practically slept with Fox News on listening for your name."

She asked me about vegetarianism and said that she loved me no matter what and would learn to cook meals without meat for when I visited. I followed her inside, feeling overwhelmed. So I went into the bathroom to sit on the edge of the tub and appreciate the Kokopelli decorations. After a few minutes, I stepped out into the hall to examine the same framed photographs of family members who served in the military as at Uncle Smileys. The upper row of portraits resembled paintings. Those men went to war. My great uncle and deceased grandfather were in the next row. Those men went to war. The next row was three of my mother's brothers who had joined and never seen combat. The final row had my two cousins whom I lived with in Nome who served in the Air National Guard, my cousin Joshua and myself. I looked into my innocent eyes and baby fat cheeks. "You thought you were so tough," I whispered. Perhaps going to war was my sole purpose in life. Maybe Smiley was right, the killings will never stop so I might as well quit trying. It is like cutting grass with scissors, a waste of time. Maybe Americans have to continuously fight on foreign soil or we will be invaded? I looked at my deceased grandfather, "How do I keep myself from self-destructing?" I stared into his intelligent, kind eyes. You were hard working, loved by everybody, with a beautiful family; yet you still drank yourself to death in a shed, I thought.

I reached into my back pocket to pull out my wallet and look at my military ID and found a folded paper towel with a note inside.

"What the hell?" I went into the bathroom to read it.

"*Vietnam 1969.*

Look God,
I have never spoken to you,
but now I want to say, "How do you do?"
You see, God, they told me you didn't exist,
and like a fool I believed all this.
Last night from my bunker I saw your sky,
I figured right then they had told me a lie.

Had I taken time to see things you made,
I'd have known they weren't calling a spade a spade.
I wonder God if you'd shake my hand;
Somehow I feel you will understand.
Funny I had no time to see your face—
Well, I guess there isn't much more to say.
I'm sure the zero hour will soon be here;
But I'm not afraid, since I know you are near.
The signal: Well God, I'll have to go—
I like you lots, this I want you to know.
Look now, this will be a horrible fight;
Who knows, I may come to your house tonight.
Though I wasn't friendly to you before, I wonder, God,
if you'd wait at your door?
Look, I'm crying! Me—shedding tears.
I wish I had known you these many years…
Well, I have to go now, God—goodbye.
Strange, since I met you, I'm not afraid to die.
Sgt. Joseph R. Moore AF 27349543
6924th Security Squadron
Drawer 54 Box 253, APO San Francisco, 96337"

I dabbed my eyes with the paper towel and took a deep breath.

"Holy shit," I whispered. "My bloodline is not only veterans and convicts, we are also poets." I folded the poem, put it in my pocket, and walked through the living room to smoke outside.

"There you are, Bobby Joe," said Grandma, like she had been looking for me. She was wearing a Cubs jacket, smoking in a lawn chair smoking. "Nobody has given you any shit tonight, have they?" She took a drink of beer from the mug she had brought from home.

"No ma'am," I said, shaking my head. "Nobody has said a word."

"Good," she said, smiling. "Ha! I told Smiley to keep his fucking mouth shut." I laughed and hugged her. I felt like I was about to cry. "I read your poem," she said. "You have real talent, kid, just like your grandpa did. Don't you go wasting it now by drinking a bunch of booze and shutting yourself off from the world."

I turned around, shed a couple of tears, and turned to face her.

"You know, kid," she said. "It's okay for men to cry, don't be fooled and think otherwise. All those old tough men you look up to from the old wars; the guys with straight faces who seem like they wouldn't cry if their baby died, I promise you—they all cry. You've got to cry after going through the shit you went through. Don't be ashamed to let it out."

"Thank you, grandma," I said, hugging her and weeping like a little bitch. "I love you so much."

"I love-a-me, too!" she said. "I got your back, kid, no matter what." She patted the back of my knee. "You're a fine young man, stay that way. I watched what booze did to my husband, your grandpa, and I don't want it to happen to you." She rattled the ice in her glass. "Some people would say that it was the war that killed him. I disagree. It wasn't the war, it was the way he handled what he had done afterward that killed him. Now run your skinny ass inside and grab your grandma another cold one."

I laughed and wiped my face.

"Have you eaten anything besides breakfast?" I asked.

"Don't worry about me, you little shit!" She smiled.

"I'm just making sure, grandma. I could make you a plate."

"Don't give me any god damn advice on how to live my life, you little shit!" She coughed spat and lit a new smoke with the old one. "Go grab me a beer and quit your yapping."

"Yes ma'am."

"You finding enough to eat around here, you little herbivore?" said Uncle Joe, smiling. He had an overflowing plate of meat resting on his extended belly. Aunt Teresa rolled her eyes and smiled.

"Not really," I replied, holding my stomach to act hungry. He looked puzzled. "Your cooking doesn't taste that great."

His eyes widened and he smiled. "You're a gosh-darn smart aleck," he said. "I don't know where you get it?"

"Yeah, who knows?" I said. "I've eaten plenty, thank you. And it's all delicious."

"Good, kid. I don't see how you do it," he said. "Must take a lot of willpower."

"How is easy," I said, "I just don't eat it, the why is a different story. Do you know why I don't eat meat, Uncle Joe?"

"For the reasons, you said earlier," he said, sucking the

meat off the bones, "but I have a funny feeling you're about to tell me another one."

I patted his belly, "Because I don't want a belly like yours."

Everybody laughed besides Smiley, who had stared at the TV the entire time.

"You little shit," said Uncle Joe. "It's good to see you. We worried about you over there, but we knew you'd be all right."

"It's good to see you guys, too," I said. "I'm on a mission to get grandma a beer."

"You do not want to make her wait," said Aunt Theresa.

Mother and I made eye contact and smiled. She looked happy, and that made me happy. I went to the freezer for a couple of ice cubes before pouring in a beer.

"It's about god damn time," said Grandma. "I almost died of dehydration!"

When the game was over and everybody was starting to leave, mother and I gave a round of hugs before loading into the Pontiac to head west.

"Did anybody ask you about Victor?" I said.

She shook her head.

"Did anybody ask you about work and Arizona?"

She shook her head.

"Did anybody ask you anything?"

She shook her head.

"I suppose it's better that way," she said.

W e took our time driving to Eugene. Stopping in Burns for breakfast after sleeping under the stars somewhere in eastern Oregon. We gazed in admiration at vast, sweeping, dry landscapes of farmland and mountains before arriving in sagebrush, ponderosa pine country. The high desert plateau on which Bend sits has a place in my heart. Hell, I got married there! We parked downtown and walked in Drake Park along the Deschutes River watching ducks burrow their bills in the mud as their cute butt feathers shook in the air. The same park where I walked with my wife and would later walk with my father. Mother loved the two towns, Bend and Sisters, and the powerful ponderosa trees. There was no mention of the fact that I had gotten married there. It's probably better that way.

We left Bend for Eugene where I was planning a reunion with my old high school buddy, Bruce Rockefeller. I was a little nervous to meet up with him, after our heavy drinking days in the past and the promise he had made me and not kept.

I was afraid that he would ask me a million questions about my time in Iraq, and try to force me into the conversation. But, I went forward with meeting up anyway.

On the outskirts of Eugene, I called him for directions to his hotel.

"The room is small," he said. "There's only one bed, but I can always make room for mom." He laughed.

"You've always had a thing for her," I said.

"Everybody has," he said. "So what?"

"Tell Bruce hello for me," said mother. "I can't wait to see him."

We found the hotel and parked. I jumped out of the car and pounded on the door. Big bad Bruce Rockefeller swung it open and picked me up with an Andre the Giant style bear hug. He had gained at least fifty pounds since I last saw him.

"You're a big bastard," I said.

"I didn't shrink any, that's for sure." He cracked every vertebrae in my spine. "I thought you'd be bigger, but you're still a little pipsqueak. Where's Mom?" He had tobacco in his upper lip, black flakes in his teeth and he smelled like beer.

"She's grabbing her things," I said.

He walked over and picked her off the ground, planting a wet kiss on her cheek.

"You're more beautiful than ever, ma," he said.

She blushed and laughed, "Thanks, son. You're looking good, too."

"Thanks, ma," he said, rubbing his belly. "Shoveling all day is building muscle, but drinking all night is gaining fat."

"I'd say," she said, patting his belly.

"I've got a couple of half racks in the fridge," he said. "Let's go inside and have a beer."

We followed Bruce inside the room.

"Congratulations on your new baby and wife," said mother. "How are they?"

"It's like living with wild cats," he said. "You never know what you're going to get. I've got a few pictures to show you, ma. The wife is crazy, and of course, our daughter takes after her."

We laughed, "You sure she doesn't get that from you?" Mother asked.

"I'm nothing compared to her," he said.

Mother and I smiled at each other as Bruce showed us the pictures of his small, red-haired baby girl.

We opened beers and slammed them against each other spilling beer onto the rug. The clock on the nightstand read thirty minutes after seven. It wasn't raining but it sure was cloudy. I didn't know what we would get into that night, but it didn't matter. We drank and laughed and forgot about the world.

Bruce wanted to go bowling. And even though mother was tired, she volunteered to be the designated driver. So we left the hotel after chugging two beers, Bruce grabbed a few for the road. He called shotgun, opened a can, took a swill, and passed it back. I drank. It felt good to be playing our old drinking game, like the entire war and military experience wasn't even real. It's like I was still a high school student skipping class to get drunk.

"Guess what happened the other night?" he said. Trying to move around in the front seat to see me, his body too damn big to do it.

"Let me guess," I said, "you were robbed by a prostitute who refused to sleep with you because you were too aggressive?"

"Nope," he said, laughing. "That's happened before though. Guess again?"

"You fell in love with a guy at work and decided to leave your wife?"

"Nope," he said. "I'm not leaving my wife." They laughed. "Last guess."

"Good guess, Robert," said mother.

"Last guess, last guess," I said. "You got in a fight and seriously injured somebody."

"What the fuck?" He said, way too loud for the small car. "How'd you know?"

"I know you, Bruce," I said, "it could only be a few options."

We finished the beer and he crushed it with his hands before opening another.

"So, I was out with some guys from school the other night," he said. "Chugging beers and bullshitting at the bar, taking turns buying shots. When one of the guys starts tossing shit in my direction. I don't know where his courage came from, but he was acting like a tough guy for no reason at all, trying to tease me in front of everybody."

"I'm sure you didn't have anything to do with it?" said mother.

Bruce let out a high pitch giggle and tried to make an innocent face.

"Me," he said, "not me, ma!"

"'You ain't got to lie to kick it,'" I said, quoting Wu-Tang.

"I was trying to simmer him down," he continued, "but I can't stand when some little bitch acts tough to show off. So I punched him in the nose and he fell straight back, like this." He held up his right hand and punched it with his left, his right elbow bent like a man falling backward. "Everybody ran to him to make sure he was okay then started calling me an asshole. I don't understand. He was the one talking shit, not me. After a few minutes, he tried to stand." He chuckled. "But his eyes were swollen shut, like yours, Bob, after that black guy knocked you out and broke your nose in high school."

"That was terrible," said mother.

"Yeah, it sucked."

"The guy's nose was pouring blood and he was rushed to the hospital. I was eighty-sixed from the bar and I might have to pay his hospital bills. I mean, what the fuck is that all about? He was the one talking shit!"

Bruce had no idea what he did wrong.

"What's going to come of it?" I asked, starting to feel a good buzz.

"The people at school want to kick me out of class and have him press charges. But he won't, he knows that he brought it on himself. The dumb ass won't talk shit, anymore."

He smiled, rolled down the window to throw out his chew, and put in another. He led us in circles searching for the bowling alley. Mother parked in a full lot. I was nervous that Bruce would make a scene, but what the hell could I do. We chugged the last beer and went inside where we were greeted by a pretty young girl at the counter.

"Hello, beautiful," said Bruce, winking. "Can we get three pairs of shoes, one lane, and two pitchers of beer?" He pulled out a hundred-dollar bill.

"Um...okay," she said, nervously. "You have to order your pitcher over there because I am only seventeen."

"Perfect," he said, looking her up and down. Mother and I smiled, shook our heads, and looked away.

"What size shoes do you need?" she asked.

"I'll take a thirteen," he said, puffing out his chest, "and what are you again, Bobby, a six in girls?" We laughed while the girl stared with a straight face.

"Let me get a pair of tens, please."

"And you, ma, what size?" He asked.

She moved her fingers together thinking and furrowed her brow.

"Hmm," she said, nibbling her cheek. "I haven't bowled in years," she blushed, "so I'm not sure what size, but I'll try a five for starters. Thanks, honey."

"It's the same as your street shoes," said the girl.

Bruce stared at her chest and licked his lips. She set the shoes on the counter and directed us to lane nine. Luckily, nobody was directly beside us. Bruce walked to the bar with his arms out wide and head held high returning with two pitchers. I plugged our information into the computer and

Mother traded shoes for a larger size. We hunted and found the perfect ball and settled into our lane.

In seventh grade, when I lived in Eagle River, I went bowling every week of the summer. It was the same summer I replaced skateboarding with rollerblading and started my first job as a paperboy. I would rollerblade a few miles downhill to town, bowl three games then call my mother to pick me up. I got to be a decent bowler and sure loved the game. Because there is not a bowling alley in Seward, it was my first time bowling with Bruce.

If our games were cutthroat, I would attempt a play-by-play, but they were not. However, I do believe that you can learn a lot about a person by the way they bowl.

Bruce used the muscle man technique, commonly referred to as the "Angry Bowler." He took three strides from starting point to release, bringing his arm and ball as high behind him as possible then flinging it down the lane so hard the parents in Lane 7 worried for their children's safety. Or maybe that was because Bruce was cussing so loud on his bad turns and shouting so loud when any of us did well. Thankfully, the father in Lane 7 didn't say anything to Bruce about his behavior, nobody did. He rarely scored strikes or spares but did succeed at drinking over a whole pitcher by the end of the first game. His high score of the night was a 69.

Mother used a soft, straight technique with more accuracy than Bruce but less power. She laughed and smiled and curtsied after every round, often saying, "I'm doing my best." Her high score was 135. She seemed to have the most fun.

I stuck to a consistent curve. I shook my head when I didn't get a spare or strike and was easily the most competitive in the group. My high score was 175.

We took a break between the second and third games to talk.

"Remember when Bruce and I used to call you in the middle of the night when we were partying to sing you songs?" I asked my mother.

"Of course, I remember," she said. "I loved it when you guys did that. You always kept your mother in mind."

"I'm still thinking about you, ma," said Bruce. "I've got so much love for you."

"Thanks, Bruce," she said, laughing. "I love you, too."

"Holy shit, Bob," said Bruce. "I almost forgot..."

"What's that?"

"To congratulate you on your marriage," he said, laughing. "And divorce."

"Fuck off."

"What the hell were you thinking?" he said. "And, where the hell was my invite?"

I contemplated telling him about trying to get over Elliot and my feelings of guilt and loneliness from the first tour, but I couldn't.

"As you both know," I said. "I have attained great wisdom in this life through firsthand experience."

They both laughed.

"How long did it last," he said. "Three weeks or three months?" I shook my head and shrugged my shoulders. "It wasn't more than three months," he continued. "So I wouldn't call you wise at all, more like impulsive."

My mother started bowling the next game. I thought about bringing up the promise Bruce made to me about signing up to fight if I ever made contact, but decided against it.

"The duration of the marriage doesn't matter," I said. "What matters is that I have learned my lesson. I didn't invite you because I knew you would fight somebody."

He laughed and nodded. "Yeah, probably," he said. "You were meant to be with Elliot, not some crazy girl from Chugiak."

"Screw Elliot," I said. "We're not meant to be. She moved on."

"Why wouldn't she?" He said. "You joined the army and got married." He held up a pitcher and I did the same. "Here's to our friendship; may we stay friends through all the fucked up shit!" Our pitchers almost cracked as we slammed them together. Beer splattered onto our table and shirts, and everybody stared. My mother grabbed napkins from the bar to clean the mess.

"What you need to do," said Bruce. "Is go to California and take her back. She's your girl, man."

"Not happening," I shook my head. "We are not in prehistoric times, Bruce. They are serious, and besides, she doesn't want anything to do with me."

"Don't give me that bullshit! You two were so in love it made everybody sick!"

"Yeah, well—that was then, this is now—times change. I've changed."

"Did she write you letters while you were away?" He asked.

I took a deep breath, wanting to go into the details about how I carried her letters in my Kevlar with her pictures and would take them out to read them, look at them, and smell them. Imagine her lying down somewhere to write me and think about me. They got me through the worst of times.

"Yeah," I said, " she wrote."

"She still loves you and always will," he said. "If there's such a thing as soulmates, you guys are them."

"Okay, boys," said mom. "Let's finish this last game, I am ready for bed."

"Yes ma'am." We echoed.

Bruce paid for everything, we could not stop him. He asked the girl for her number and she said it was against policy. He tried to talk mom into taking us to a strip club but she laughed and said, "Not tonight, Bruce." We went back to the hotel where Bruce hugged her and told her that he loved her before singing "You Are My Sunshine" with me as a backup. She wiped her eyes with a paper towel and went to sleep in the car. It was the last time they saw each other. (Ten years after this story, I called Bruce to tell him that my mother was dying from lung cancer. She cried on the phone with him and told him that she loved him like a son and called him a sweet young man. I swear I heard him crying on the other end.)

I packed my sleeping bag, toiletries, pen, and paper in a backpack and went inside to drink until passing out. I awoke the next morning on the floor with a pounding headache as Bruce crashed around the room like a huge tank in a tiny village. He used the microwave, knocked over a lamp, took a shower with the door open, and said goodbye. I rolled to my side and faced the wall, inspecting the carpet for cleanliness. A pebble was near my face, I had slept on a big stain on the carpet. I remembered the time we spent three days searching villages without finding a single weapon. We finally laid down to sleep on the sand by our trucks after dark. We shivered all night, it was so damn cold. I woke up multiple times the final night with something jabbing into my back, but I didn't want to take the sleeping bag off my head because I was so cold. So I tried to sleep through it. When we got up with the sun the next morning, we discovered that I had slept on an AK-47 buried in the sand; we all got a good laugh at that.

I passed back out on the floor and woke up sometime later covered in sweat. I could not remember what I was dreaming, but I could feel the dreams. I dumped the pack on the floor searching for the pen and paper. Out fell a handful of cigarette butts and dirty socks. I lay on the floor writing as tears and sweat stained the carpet.

Where are you now, God?
We pray for you every night.
Where are you now, God?
Again, nowhere in sight.
Where are you now, God?
We need you more than ever.

Where are you now, God?
Men's heads are being severed.
Where are you now, God?
In this everlasting darkness called war.
Where are you now, god?
Are you allowing all this horror?

I stared at the paper with a shaky pen and chicken skin. Rubbing my hair and beard to relax, they were longer than they had been in years. I started drawing an infinity symbol in the top right-hand corner of the page; a technique the psychics taught me back in the day to engage spirits for automatic writing.

The Holy Ghost is upon me in the middle of the night.
As I walk alone,
No one protects me
From unyielding temptations
Of the angel of darkness.
I have hurt those who love me
A void in each one's soul.
No wonder I am all alone,
I will never fill the hole.

"Fuck those motherfuckers who sent us," I said, standing up to pace before stepping out to light a smoke. "I hope they die miserable deaths." I smoked half of it before rushing inside to continue.

The other day I watched a man die who had been shot
in the throat.
Growing up the way I did I always thought
I would see some fairly gruesome things
but I had never imagined that.
The man was helpless.
Shot by a racist hick who claimed that he was firing a
'warning shot,'
I know the truth.
We are not allowed to fire warning shots, we
shoot to kill.
He was unarmed,
stealing supplies with his brother
from an abandoned cement factory.
The blood gushed
we could not stop it.
Dressing after dressing could not stop
the life force from spurting out of him.
I watched him struggle for survival while
slowly giving in to the undefeated desires of death.
He was white when we loaded him
into the humvee,
his eyes piercing the back of his skull,
life sucked right out of him. Gravity taking control.
It was the first time I watched a man die,
not the last.
The guy who shot him feels no remorse,
laughing afterward he claimed:

'I swear I was aiming two inches over his head'
with the thickest southern drawl and lazy eye
in Kirkuk.
He filled sandbags in the sun for a week
as punishment for murder.
At this point, I don't know if I am on the
good side or the bad side.
I do know one thing, though,
I'm confused as all hell.

Tears fell on the carpet like bombs on Baghdad. I was exhausted. I shoved the notebook and pen away, turned on the shower, closed the drain, and lay in hot water. I needed to stop being such a pussy and drive on. Why the hell did I drink so much? I need to quit, there are too many ups and downs. It is not worth feeling like shit. If I could stop after one or two, it would be okay, but I can't. I lay in my sorrow for about thirty minutes before brushing my teeth and making a pot of coffee. I went to wake up mother with a steamy cup and stopped to smile at the thick, dark clouds that reminded me that I was not the only one having a storm. Rain glistened on concrete and mist was in the air. I breathed deeply and felt good to be in the Pacific Northwest, I almost started crying but had to get my shit together. The car was locked, so I tapped on the window.

"Good morning, mother. It's time to wake up."

There was rustling. She opened the door and stretched her arms out.

"Morning, son," she said. "Thanks for letting me sleep in."

"No problem," I said, handing her the cup of coffee.

"Thank you," she said, excitedly.

"How'd you sleep?" I asked.

"Hard," she said, stepping onto the wet concrete with bare feet. She rubbed her eyes. "I forgot how nice it is to sleep in a car with rain on the roof," she said. "It put me right to sleep." She hugged me. "When did you boys finally get to bed?"

"Oh, I'm not exactly sure," I said, skipping the fact that I blacked out. "What do you think about walking around town before heading to the coast?"

"We can find a bookstore and a place to eat," she said.

"That sounds great," I said. "And tonight, we can sleep by the ocean!"

She put on her glasses and opened the trunk.

"It's a plan," she said, "but first things first. I need to use the lady's room."

She went inside and I looked in the side mirror just long enough to feel guilty before scanning the hotel's roof and doorways. I sipped my coffee and smoked a few cigarettes while staring at the sky until she came out. We drove slowly through tree-lined neighborhoods covered in yellow and red leaves admiring the houses before parking downtown to mosey.

After I was asked three times for spare change by people my age, I was pissed.

"Those lazy bums need to get a job," I said.

"It wouldn't hurt any," she said. "But maybe some of

them can't work. Not everybody has the mental and physical capacity that we do. We need to remember, that just because a person looks healthy doesn't mean they are." She gave away five dollars that day.

A rain squall struck so we tucked inside a pizza parlor to split a large vegetarian and read the local paper.

"I hope those kids stay dry out there," she said. "It must be hard not to have a home."

Did I have a home? I wondered. My home was my car.

"Hey son," she said, with an innocent look. "You wouldn't mind driving today, would ya?"

"Of course not," I said. "I love to drive."

33

We cruised west in silent admiration of the mountains and forest until finally we made it to Newport and parked on a bluff overlooking the beach. The sound of the waves brought comfort and strength. The sound of the seagulls brought present moment awareness. We drove south and found a beach access point to walk barefooted while listening and watching the waves crash. I gathered sand dollars, felt like a kid, and forgot about war altogether. We sat on a log to watch sandpipers run in and out of the water with their tiny feet making delicate sounds. What were they searching for? I wondered. Would they find it? Being in Oregon made me feel at home.

We traveled south on Highway 1 through North Bend and Coos Bay, stopping at Port Orford for a cup of coffee before continuing past huge rocks that seem to have been strewn about by Gods in no particular order. We walked barefooted at Gold Beach, where my mother mentioned my father was born. I hoped to see him, to meet him, hug him, and be told how proud of me he is. But none of that happened, instead, I chased the waves as Mother used her camera to make small things look big and big things look small. The wishing and washing of the water seemed to wipe away my past. The wind on my face blew the corners of my lips upward. A handful of people were on the beach with happy dogs chasing happy birds. I monitored them for a moment before realizing that I was paranoid and was certainly not in danger. I closed my eyes to absorb the sun and space.

A gust of wind ripped my hat off and I chased it down the beach as mother laughed. I watched the ocean for sea creatures; whales, flying fish, great whites, giant squid, sea otters, sea lions, mermaids, boats, Poseidon, anything; but there was nothing to focus on besides vast space. So I stared and felt good. I thought about Brammer, Sully, and Alvarez and hoped they were doing well. I wondered whatever came of Loveall. I hoped that the burned children in Iraq were healed and that the crying man who held his dying brother had found peace. I hoped that the interpreter from Florida made enough money to return home to live comfortably and that the guys who peed on those bodies forgave themselves in time. I was grateful for the Kurdish people and hoped they one day had a home. I wondered about the landfill during my second tour that was full of brand new air conditioners, televisions, and other expensive electronics. Had it been cleaned up and reused? I hoped that the divisions between Sunni, Shi'a, Kurd, Muslim, Christian, Hindu, and Buddhist were merged. We are all united under the clouds. Finally, I hoped for peace of mind.

An old man stepped in front of me to take pictures with a Canon Rebel. He did not look back or offer an apology like he didn't even realize I was there. He backpedaled until within arms reach, and I thought about tripping him and kicking him in the face. But then I felt guilty for thinking such things. So I focused on his deeply lined neck, long ponytail, and loose left pant leg. He turned and smiled, he was wearing a Vietnam Veteran hat.

"Sure is peaceful," he said. "It's an honor to live in this country."

And he walked away. I stared at his back while wondering what type of hell had he been through. Were we at Gold Beach for the same reason, to transcend guilt through appreciation of nature? If he can drive on, so can I.

Mother returned from a photographic excursion.

"I just may have captured the moment," she said. "We'll see when we get home."

I put my arm around her shoulders.

"You know that I love you, ma," I said, squeezing her.

"I love you, too, son." She smiled.

"Thanks for everything you did while I was growing up," I said. "I was a little asshole."

"Not all the time." We laughed.

"And for sending all of those packages while I was in Iraq," I said. "It may have saved my life."

Her eyes had tears and she turned toward the ocean. Seagulls glided low over waves.

"Thank you for all your help," she said. "I could not have moved without you."

With my left arm around her shoulders and her right arm around my hips, we watched the sun sink below the horizon as thousands of tiny crabs scurried between tiny holes at our feet.

For a moment, I reflected on the fact that by the time I was twenty, I had pointed a rifle into hundreds of people's faces. By the time my brother was twenty, he was the leader of a prison gang. We sure kept our family traditions alive. Are we the best sons and people that we can be?

Mother radiated serenity within the redwood forest. It was a clear day, a great day for driving. We rolled down the windows, slowed to forty-five, and absorbed our surroundings. We took the scenic route, stopping a half dozen times to hug trees and take pictures. Yes, we are a family of tree huggers. I leaned on my heels to try to see the treetops and nearly fell over backward tripping on exposed roots. I was comforted being surrounded by three-thousand-year-old beings that had lived through wildfires, clear cuts, earthquakes, insect infestations, human beings, and God knows what else. It was like being in Jurassic Park without being chased by velociraptors. I pressed my nose deep into cracks in the bark and inhaled. Ahhh… It brought peace and comfort. I wanted to bottle it up to smell all day and night.

Whose feet or paws had pattered these trails? I wondered. Which birds nested in these limbs? We walked a trail toward nowhere without words, not as scientists or discoverers, but as human beings. We stopped in Crescent City to visit Paul Bunyan and Blue, moseying through the gift shop and museum trying to focus on the beauty of the Native American art instead of the sadness of their colonization. It was difficult to do.

My mother bought three magnets and postcards that read,

"*A Giant Sequoia's Guide to Life:*
Have a thick skin
Stand up to the heat
Don't let things bug you
Heal your own wounds
Enjoy your days in the sun
Strive for balance
Hold yourself up high."

We left, and my eyes roamed as I drifted within inches of the guard rail.

"Be careful son," said mother. "Don't run us into the ditch."

"Sorry," I said, overcorrecting. "I can't keep my eyes from the ocean and trees. I've been dreaming of this for years."

"There's nothing better than being next to the ocean," she said. "Watching and listening to waves cleanse our souls. If you want me to drive, I will."

"I'm okay ma," I said. "I'll pay closer attention to the road."

I stared into taillights while white and yellow lines flashed in my periphery. Tears formed. Mother asked if everything was okay and I said it was, yet deep down I felt like nothing would ever be okay. I tried to admire the coastline, but all I could see was the innocent Iraqi's dying face, the little boy with elephantiasis, and a mirage of screaming women covering their faces with burkhas as I stormed inside their home.

You're driving, Robert, I told myself, in America. Get your shit together.

I couldn't stop thinking about rolling through Mosul, Irbil, and Kirkuk. A sea of smiling faces filled with joy. They were free and happy. Two years later, when I returned for my second deployment, locals held signs that read: "Fuk Amrika," and "Give us back our cuntry!" And, I too, wanted to give them back their country. Saddam had been captured and executed. There were no weapons of mass destruction. Innocent Iraqis were killed every day by terrified Americans. People didn't wave and smile, they glared. I thought about the poor Africans and Sri Lankans who were paid two dollars an hour to cook and serve us food while American contractors made hundreds of thousands of dollars to write our names on a list to use the phone and internet. I am an invader; responsible for spreading white supremacy and colonialism, for ruining an ancient way of life. I enforced curfews, kicked down doors, elbowed holes in walls, patrolled streets and pissed on corners, and forced people to wait hours in the blistering heat for water, propane, and gasoline. I ripped through people's homes and vehicles, hid in ambush sites waiting to kill, left toxic waste in the form of depleted uranium, and drove through farmer's fields laughing at their misfortune and dumb simplicity. I killed two police officers who fired at me from a white Toyota pickup with red letters. Didn't I?

I pulled into a rest stop.

"Is everything all right, son?"

"Please quit fucking asking me that," I said.

My mother stepped outside to take a walk and use the restroom.

I hardly slept that night, I chain-smoked instead. I glared at the smiling face in the moon and became pissed off at myself for being pissed off at myself.

How the hell would I make it as a civilian? What the fuck was I going to do?

After sunrise, we continued south under clear skies. I felt a little better. I was going to be okay. Mother had to get back to work and I had to get back to Alaska. We crossed the Golden Gate Bridge into San Francisco, parked by the piers, and walked around. Mother took pictures of Alcatraz while I thought about how lucky James was that he didn't do time in California, just like I am lucky that I didn't fight in Vietnam, Korea, or a World War. The shame I had for snitching on him back in middle school had been replaced by anger and indifference. He decided to use drugs, run with thugs, and rob a liquor store, not me. He would have been caught anyway. As if my mother could read my mind, she said, "I spoke with your brother yesterday. He says, 'Hello, and that he can't wait to see you in Alaska.'"

I nodded, "That'll be nice."

I tried not to stare at the hundreds of beautiful women

but it was impossible not to. We watched skaters do tricks at a famous spot I grew up watching on videos; watched sea lions bark and people load on ferries headed for Alcatraz. The smell of perfume and saltwater excited me. We shared clam chowder in a bread bowl then walked up streets that smelled like urine to Chinatown to eat lunch on a balcony and buy five shirts for ten dollars. We visited City Lights Bookstore and drank an Irish Stout at a bar nearby. I imagined Ginsberg, Kerouac, and Snyder sharing a pitcher. Mother insisted on taking a picture of me under Jack Kerouac Street. We avoided drug addicts and pimps in the Soma District and walked past Candlestick Park to the car. It was a long walk, much needed after so much sitting.

We continued south to visit a huge-hearted hippie friend of mothers named Diane in Santa Cruz whose thirty-three-year-old son was locked away for a murder he did not commit. She met my mother in the Coolidge waiting room two years prior after she came over for a two-week visiting room vacation. The next day, she paid an early check-out fee at the motel to stay at her mother's trailer for free. Similarities in their lives were evident, they bonded deeply while sharing stories over glasses of wine and Corona with lime.

We followed her rusty old Toyota Camry to a single-story hotel with two beds, a shower, and a sink. Diane paid for the room in return for my mother's hospitality. She was older than fifty with blue eyes, strong hands, and straight silver hair past her lower back. She made a living as a natural healer, specializing in crystals and massage. She was unhappily married to "an asshole on disability who sits around the house all day drinking beer and watching television."

Diane left us at the hotel to clean up, agreeing to pick us up in an hour to stroll the boardwalk. After watching The Lost Boys a dozen times as a kid, I was excited to see the boardwalk and carnival. I was thankful for a soft bed and hot shower. Mother showered first while I watched cable from bed. She brushed her hair while I showered. Diane picked us up in a tie-dye summer skirt and white cardigan. She had a bottle of wine in her purse, a smile on her face, and a big glow of excitement.

"I almost forgot," she said, digging in her purse. "I have something for you."

"For me?" I said. Why the hell would she have something for me? I wondered.

She pulled out a ticket stub and a tee shirt.

"Twenty years ago I went to a concert at The Catalyst that changed my life," she said. "It was the father of this man." She handed me a ticket that read: "Entrance for one to Ziggy Marley."

"Holy shit," I said. "You saw Bob Marley?"

"Yes sir," she said. "Probably before you were born, too. This is a gift, for you. Ziggy is playing tonight at The Catalyst and I thought you should see him."

My jaw dropped. What could I say? I tried to hand it back but she refused.

"I can't accept this," I said. "You two should go."

"Sure you can," she said. "And you will." I bowed and

clutched the ticket to my heart. "You will remember this night for the rest of your life," she said. "Let the music change you."

I thanked her and hugged her.

"You're going to have so much fun, son," said mother.

Diane unfolded a black shirt with a sun covered by a half lion, half Bob Marley face.

"I wore this shirt to Bob and the Wailers twenty-five years ago," she said. "I want you to have it."

I shook my head, I couldn't understand.

"Why me?" I said. "I am the furthest thing from *one love.*"

"If you're anything like your mother," she said, "you have a golden heart. You just need to open it. Please, take it." I changed shirts. And to top it all off, she handed me a pack of cigarettes with five pre-rolled joints.

We roamed around the carnival listening to people scream on rides as pattering feet walked on wood. The sexiest woman I have ever seen played volleyball in a bikini. I stared at her and nearly drooled. Two young girls shared cotton candy with pink smiles. For a moment, perhaps the first moment of my life, I felt proud to have served my country. I felt proud to be an American.

The ladies split off for dinner and drinks before going to the theater to watch the new Robin Williams movie where he played the President. Mother loved Robin Williams. I smoked two joints near the bike path with a young guy from Nebraska who always dreamed of living on the beach. He was now living the dream. I got super stoned and stashed the pack of joints at the base of a light pole before passing through the relaxed security at the venue. A fog of marijuana smoke engulfed the place and seemed to bring everybody together. People passed joints the size of fifty caliber rounds and I smoked them. When Ziggy was on stage, I closed my eyes and felt like I was listening to Bob. When he sang Redemption Song, tears streamed down my face; I felt like a pirate who had robbed them and sold them to merchant ships. I needed redemption.

I was covered in sweat with cloudy eyes when I left the show after dark. I grabbed the joints and smoked on the beach under the stars while listening to the waves crash and people laugh. I smiled at the change of events. Less than a month before I was in Iraq, afraid for my life; now, I was smoking a joint on a beach in California after dancing at a reggae concert.

Mother was asleep by the time I made it to the room and passed out hard.

We spent a few hours the next day on a beach with Diane south of Santa Cruz. Mother drove in traffic that lasted three hours around the black cloud of Los Angeles. I drove east into a wind storm in Arizona, passed three big rigs tipped over on their sides. Tumbleweeds bounced across the road as raindrops the size of golf balls struck the windshield, followed by hail. I was ready for shattered glass. We arrived at Mother's trailer around three in the morning the following day and went straight to bed.

35

Paul arrived after breakfast with a brand new roof rack for my Subaru.

"Here's a little goodbye gift for ya," he said. "I figured you could use more room in the back to lie down. It would be uncomfortable sleeping in the front all the way to Alaska, and you need good rest if you're driving that far."

He helped install it and insisted on buying new brakes. He changed them and I helped, and then he lent me tools to change my oil. I moved the black footlocker and change container to the roof and had enough space to spread out blankets, pillows, and a sleeping bag. I thanked him deeply, and never saw him again.

My mother spent most of the day visiting her husband. It didn't bother me like it used to. After watching the sunset and eating dinner, I received a call from a friend in Yuma whom I planned to visit on the way north.

"How's it going?" she asked, with a quiet voice. "You ready to go home?"

"Oh yeah," I said, "saying goodbye to mother is never fun, but I'm making the best of it. How are you?"

"Well," she said, taking a deep breath. "Did you hear?"

"Hear what?"

"About Jessi… Jessi Thorson died last night."

"What the hell happened?"

"She was driving in the wrong direction on a bypass."

I took a deep breath and held the phone away from my ear. When Elliot and I started dating in high school, Jessi's twin sister had recently died in a car accident, and Elliot would listen to the Sarah McLachlan song, "Arms of an Angel" every night in bed.

"Have you talked to Elliot?" I said.

"She was in Bangkok," she said. "It was her second day of a three-month trip. She changed her ticket and is flying into LA tomorrow."

LA is not far from where I am, I thought. What I would give to see her.

"She's meeting with Chris and Jason tomorrow, they're all driving to Vegas for the services."

I couldn't stand the thought of Chris comforting her.

"It's in Vegas, huh?" I said. "How are you holding up?"

"I can't imagine how their parents feel," she said. "First they lose Mel, and now Jessi, both in car accidents." She sniffled. "There's not much to say. I hope the sisters are together, wherever they are."

"Yeah, me too," I said. "Me too."

"So, you should stay the night here then head to Vegas for the service," she said. "I'm sure Elliot would love to see you."

"But she has Chris now," I said. "I don't think I could handle seeing them together."

"She would love to see you," she said. "They all would."

"Okay," I said. "I'll head to your place tomorrow, and then to Vegas."

I hung up and sat in silence. When I came out, my mother handed me a root beer float in an icy mug.

Dear Mother,

Thank you for the amazing trip! For driving when I
was too sore and sleeping in front when I needed to
stretch. I will never forget the feeling of freedom and
adventure we shared on the open road. You are the
best mother a son could ask for. Thanks for everything.

With Endless Love,

Your son,
Robert

I left the note on the counter, double-checked that I had
everything, and left. The Subaru looked like a brand new
car with a roof rack. I patted the hood, opened the door, and
put the key in the ignition. Rubbing the dashboard for luck,
I started her up and listened to the putter of the engine with
clean oil. "John Brown" played on the speakers and I turned it

up, I had missed Bob Dylan. I did not want to leave Mother
again, and I was afraid to see Elliot; not to mention, I was
nervous to get home in case I did not fit in anymore. But all
I could do was focus on one thing at a time, and I needed
to do something otherwise I would sink into depression. I
left the trailer park and went to Safeway for snacks and to
say goodbye. She was in work mode, so I went to the deli to
order a sandwich to go.

The deli worker was a dark-skinned woman my age who
looked familiar, but I could not pinpoint it. She wore a name
tag that said, Sarah. When she finished ringing up a man
with a trimmed goatee, snakeskin boots, and cowboy hat,
she turned to me.

"What would you like?" She asked with an accent I
somehow recognized.

"A vegetarian sandwich with pesto on focaccia, please,
double the mozzarella."

Her soft, dark hands sliced the bread.

"How long have you lived in Coolidge?" I asked.

She looked at me skeptically.

"I have been here," she said, pointing the knife at the
ground, "for two years."

"Of all the places in the world, why Coolidge?"

She smiled. She had beautiful brown eyes and dark lips.
Her teeth were so white they glowed. She glanced around
before delicately setting mozzarella discs on pesto. The green
and white colors looked pretty together.

"Too many reasons to explain," she said.

"Okay," I said. "Where were you before here?"

"New York City," she said, "before that, Florida."

"How did you like New York?" I asked. "I love Harlem, it's my favorite part of town."

"The buildings are very tall," she said. "They are beautiful, no doubt, but they block the sun and stars. Where I am from, you can always see the sky."

"Yeah, me too," I said.

"Where are you from?" She asked, adding lettuce and tomatoes.

"Alaska," I replied. "I'm on my way home right now."

"Alaska," she said. "It is very cold in Alaska, yes?"

"Oh yeah," I said. "I love the cold, though. I am used to it. Where are you from?"

She hesitated while looking into my eyes.

"Northern Iraq," she said. "Irbil, to be exact."

I shook my head. "No way."

"You probably do not know where it is, do you?"

I laughed, "Oh yeah, I know where it is."

"How you do know?" she looked puzzled. "Nobody knows Irbil."

"I was there in 2003," I said. "During the invasion."

"Me, too." We looked at each other and smiled. Soul mates. "What were you doing, and what brought you here?"

"I was infantry," I said. "I am here to visit my mother. Will you go back to Irbil? With everything happening over there, it seems like a dangerous place to live."

She punched numbers into the register as I pulled out my wallet.

"I will never go back," she said. "Certain people hate me for what I did for the American government. If my family returns, we will be killed."

I shook my head. "Where are your parents? What did you do?"

"Here in Coolidge," she said. "I went to university in Kirkuk to be a chemist and a translator of the English language. I was a professional in Iraq. But now, in America, I can only work in grocery stores and gas stations. I cannot use my education because I cannot say where I am from. When employers see my application and hear my accent, they assume I am a terrorist. Everybody assumes this. They do not realize that I helped the United States."

"I'm sorry to hear that," I said. "This country was built on racism, it runs deep like perennial roots."

"Yes," she said, "but even perennial roots can be destroyed." I nodded. "Your total is seven dollars and fifty-eight cents."

I handed her a twenty.

"Thank you for the sandwich," I said, "and the talk. I will not forget you."

She blushed, and I almost broke down in tears.

"Yes you will," she said.

I turned and walked down artificial aisles toward the exit, giving my mother a tear-stained hug before stepping outside to light a smoke.

I recalled seeing a field of cotton outside of town. It was

my first time seeing cotton grown, while I had heard songs and read poems about the painful work of picking cotton, I had never seen it. I wanted to know what it felt like on my fingers and body, even if only for an hour. Yeah, I would be stealing and trespassing, and I was not under a whip or stripped of all human dignity, so the circumstances were vastly different. But still, I wanted the experience; and I wanted to make a pillow for my friend's newborn son.

By the time I found the field and started picking, it was not even ten and the sun felt like it was burning a hole in the back of my neck. I removed my shirt and picked fast to avoid an angry farmer. I was filling a pillowcase, and I quickly realized the arduousness of the task. Cotton balls stuck to thorny branches and as I tried to pick faster I became more clumsy. Until blood dripped from my fingertips into the soil, and I wondered how many other people had spilled blood in that exact place. Moisture from the cotton soaked into my pores. Sweat fell. Thorny branches stuck into my clothes and skin and it was hard to move from plant to plant. I picked until my face and shoulders were burnt and the pillowcase half full. I picked until I could no longer pick comfortably. How privileged I am.

I set the pillowcase in the passenger seat and drove towards Yuma looking south out the open window across a vast desert toward Mexico. I wanted to travel through Copper Canyon and explore the Sierra Madres. I wanted to travel further south into Central and South America. I wanted to live.

A strip mall appeared like a mirage, and I realized that I needed fabric to make the pillow so I bought a blue Osh Kosh B' Gosh handkerchief and left.

On the outskirts of Yuma, I called for directions.

My friend and her mother were outside of their trailer to greet me when I arrived. The newborn was asleep in a crib in the back room. We hovered over him admiring his cuteness. His tiny face resembled his father's, my friend in Seward whose parents used to let us drink at their house. I laughed at the resemblance.

"He looks just like him, doesn't he?" my friend asked.

"One hundred percent," I said.

What will you do in this lifetime? I wondered. Will you be another lost son without a father to show him the ropes? Will you respect and take care of your mother and other women? Will you be honest, hardworking, dependable, loving, and compassionate? Will you meet somebody and fall in love?

"Are you hungry?" asked my friend's bald mother, clutching her hands over her recently removed breasts with a look of concern. "We haven't made anything for lunch, but you are more than welcome to make yourself something."

"Thanks," I said. "I'm okay right now."

We walked into the kitchen and living room.

"How was your trip with your mama?" The mother asked.

"Life-changing," I said. "She glowed the entire way."

"You are glowing yourself," she said. "Do you want to hang out on the patio?"

"Sure," I said. "I have to grab some things first."

I noticed framed pictures of family members on the wall; three sisters, a mother, grandparents, and a boat. I grabbed the cloth and pillowcase and went around back to sit under a vine-covered lattice on the patio.

"What do you have there?" My friend asked, smiling.

"Nothing," I said.

"I don't believe you," she said, laughing. "It can't be more surprising than when you shit in a Mason jar and gave it to me wrapped as a birthday present when we were in high school."

"You asked for it," I said.

"I wasn't serious!"

"I didn't know that," I said.

"I am more careful about what I ask for," she said.

"I just have a little cotton," I said. "To make a pillow for Jack."

I held open the pillowcase and they looked inside and laughed.

"Where the hell did you get cotton?"

"From a cotton field."

They waited for an explanation and after a few seconds, my friend said, "You are a crazy, crazy man, Bob Stark, one of a kind."

"It'll be a Christmas gift," I said.

"There's some fresh lavender near where you parked," said her mother. "Add some to make it smell nice."

We sat in a circle sorting seeds from fluff, avoiding hard topics like Jessi's death, Iraq, and cancer. We tossed seedless cotton balls into a straw basket between us.

"It's one thing to catch your limit," I said. "It's another thing to clean them."

"It will be worth it when he has a handmade pillow," said the mother.

The strain on my hands made me wonder about slaves and immigrant farmworkers in America. How many had carpal tunnel and other painful ailments and diseases without access to medicine? How many still do?

"We can't have pokey little seeds puncture the skin of a fragile baby while he sleeps himself bigger," the mother said, smiling. She painfully stood and walked inside.

"It's a damn shame about Jessi," I said, lighting a cigarette. "So young."

"Yeah it is," she said, shaking her head. "But, you know— maybe she is in a better place. Maybe she is with her sister."

"Maybe," I said. "It's comforting to think so, that's for sure."

"You're going to the service, right?"

"Yeah, I'll leave in the morning," I said. "I always wanted to avoid Vegas, but this is some kind of coincidence."

"I wish I could come," she said, "but I have school, and the baby, and I want to be around to help mother. She would never admit it, but she needs the help."

"We all do sometimes."

I grabbed the bowl of cotton and added lavender to the mix.

"You guys ready to eat?" Her mother poked her head out of the sliding glass door.

We went inside to a set table with a colorful salad,

spaghetti with homemade marinara, and garlic bread. After dinner, the mother pulled out a Singer from the corner, and in ten minutes, the baby pillow was finished. I set it beside his delicate face and smiled at having done something nice for somebody.

I woke up in the dark reaching for my rifle. It had fallen from my fingertips into the sand as we chased a man in a tractor. Was it just a dream? I wondered. After a few breaths, I smelled bacon and coffee and was reminded of being in Yuma with friends not in Iraq. We ate breakfast, I skipped the bacon, and I drank two glasses of raw goat's milk and three cups of coffee. Baby Jack joined us in a high chair and made a huge mess of the syrup. It was the first time I had been around a baby since I could remember, and it was a strange feeling to be around such a new and innocent life after being around so much destruction and death.

After breakfast, I thanked them and said goodbye. Driving the flat endless road to Las Vegas, I kept my eyes peeled for roadside bombs and donkey carts, swerving around potholes. My jaw dropped and my neck ached as I stared up at extravagant hotels and buildings on the Vegas strip. It was an incredible work of architectural artistry. Jessi's parents paid for a room at the Excalibur for "the Alaskans" to share, so I parked in the lot and laid in the back of the car to read some Gary Snyder and hopefully calm my nerves before seeing Elliot. It would be my first time seeing her with Chris, and my first time seeing Chris and Jason since Iraq.

When I finally gathered the courage to call and meet, the three of them met me in the lobby of the hotel where Elliot and I awkwardly shook hands. It was the same with Chris, my old high school buddy. Jason and I hugged, but it was evident that his loyalty was divided. Everything was different. I was different. They went to separate tables to gamble while I left the casino to buy a bottle of whiskey. I drank half of the bottle in the front seat of the car and then stumbled around the streets smoking. I bought a bag of "weed" from a stranger that ended up being lint, I still smoked it. I stumbled into the casino after who knows how long and found Jason at the same blackjack table while Elliot and Chris sat beside each other on bar stools. She wept, he held her. I couldn't stand it, I left to wander in sadness and rage. I wanted to hold her while she cried; I wanted to rub her back and kiss her forehead; I wanted to comfort her like she had comforted me so many lonely nights while I was in Iraq. I laid in the back of the car and smoked while battling the spins until finally passing out.

In the middle of the night, I got up and stood on the sidewalk saying hello to everybody who passed but nobody said hello back. Didn't they know I fought for this country? I thought. To help preserve their Deep Fried Twinkie way of life. I passed out again and slept until morning.

I drove to the cemetery chapel a few hours later underdressed, unknown and unwanted. Elliot's low-hung head and tattooed shoulders were in the front row beside other girlfriends of Jessi's. Every one of them was crying. Jessi's parents had puffy eyes and drenched faces. I felt for them, and for the Iraqis who lost children. Just as I sat down in the last pew as a stranger, a man started singing, "Jessi's Girl" while playing the keyboard. Tears streamed down his face, everybody wept. Jessi's body was covered in flowers and hidden in a white casket at the front of the room. I stared at the beautiful flowers and realized that I had not seen a flower in many years. That I hadn't seen a single flower while I was in Iraq or even while in Italy, Tennessee, or any other country for that matter. I had been so lost in fear, alcohol, and searching for a false sense of masculinity that I hadn't taken the time to see any flowers at all. They were so colorful and delicate, soft and sturdy, thorny and aromatic. I could smell them from the back of the room. They brought light to a dark time. Out of nowhere, I began to cry, too. I cried for my childhood longing for my father and the search for a replacement in Dan and Victor; I cried for my lost innocence when my baseball coach tried to rape me; I cried for my brother, who did way too long inside a prison cell as only a child; I cried for the alcoholic identity I had created for myself in high school because I was too afraid to try academically; I cried for the childhood baseball star who never picked up a glove again; I cried for the times I was bullied for my speech impediment as a little boy and for the time my brother picked up the snowball and

318

burst open my stitches; I cried for the sacrifices my mother made to ensure I had a roof over my head; I cried for the neglect she received from Dan and the way she was treated by my brother; I cried for the disillusioned belief that I would join the army to help people and yet all I did was bring fear and destruction; and eventually, I cried for Jessi and her sister and their family.

Where are you now, God? I wondered. Why is she dead instead of me?

After the memorial, people reunited at the reception area which was held in an upstairs portion of a restaurant. I shared a table with "the Alaskans" and other friends of Jessi's, awkwardly watching a slideshow of her short life with background music. It crushed me to sit at the same table as Elliot and not be able to talk with her and touch her. I wanted to jump off a cliff and die. When "Arms of an Angel" played, I went to the bar to order a whiskey. The girls' laughed and sobbed when pictures of them with Jessi came on screen. Chris wiped Elliot's cheeks with a handkerchief and she smiled at him with puffy eyes. I wanted to strangle him with the handkerchief, but I was also grateful that he was taking such good care of her. Way better care than I had. The girls held each other, the men did their best to keep a straight face, and I went outside to smoke. When I came back inside, Jason met me at the drink station and put his hand on my shoulder.

"I fucking love you, Bob," he said. "I'm so happy you made it back home alive. I was worried sick about you, man."

I nodded, "I love you, too, man. Thanks"

"Where did you come back from?" Asked the pretty girl who was serving us. She had big curly blonde hair, green eyes, and white gloves.

"Nowhere," I said. "I haven't made it back yet."

Everybody drank heavy and laughed hard. Elliot was so beautiful I could not look at her, but I could smell her patchouli and fresh rain oil from across the table. It drove me crazy. Jessi's fiancé arrived with his head hung and shoulders slumped. He dragged his feet to our table and the girls stood to hug him. He was wearing a black button-up shirt, black jeans, and black skate shoes with scuff marks on his right foot. He was obviously goofy-footed. He looked like somebody who wanted to be left alone yet needed somebody to talk with. He stared at the table and drank without looking at the slideshow screen.

"Does anybody want to smoke weed?" He said. "I have a lot."

Glances shot back and forth, shoulders shrugged and heads shook. Elliot looked at me for what felt like the first time in years and I almost crumbled.

"I'll smoke with you," I said.

"Let's meet outside in five minutes," he said, barely above a whisper.

"Take your time," I said. "I can wait." I patted Jason's shoulder and left.

I waited outside behind the door smoking with my foot against the wall. People left without noticing me, they supported each other like I had heard people do during times of grief. Jason and Chris left without seeing me and

I wondered where Elliot was. A few minutes later, she came outside and glanced around. We locked eyes and time stopped. The girl who saw past the bullshit and loved me; who wrote hundreds of letters to remind me that I was not forgotten; whose pictures and words I carried in a plastic bag in my Kevlar helmet and vest to admire when alone or afraid; the girl whose smell put me to sleep for years. We stared at each other for what seemed like hours before she walked over to me and leaped into my arms. We hugged as hard as two people can without injury, her feet were off the ground. I kissed the top of her head, smelled her hair, and cried.

"I missed you so much," she said, sniffling. "I was so worried."

"I missed you, too," I said. "Thanks for the letters."

We wiped each others' eyes and smiled.

"You're still the same person," she said, rubbing my face. "But now you have a beard."

I dropped my head and half laughed half cried. I did not feel like the same person.

"It's my first beard," I said. "I think I am a man."

She laughed and touched my face, "You're still just a boy." She wiped tears from her eyes, glanced behind her, and stepped back. "I have to go," she said. "Chris is waiting."

I took a deep breath and nodded.

She stepped forward and ran her fingers through my hair.

"I have dreamed of this for years," she said.

I dropped my head and cried, "Me, too."

She gently lifted my chin and looked past my guilt and shame with those hazel, bloodshot eyes I knew so well.

"I will always love you, Bob," she said. "Please don't forget that, okay?"

I nodded and wept.

She kissed me on the lips, and I kissed her back, and then she took two steps back and stared at me like she used to, like Marlena did, like I was still an innocent boy worthy of love, before she turned around to walk away.

EPILOGUE

March 26, 2022

I am writing this epilogue from my quiet home in the Alaskan countryside, nineteen years to the day after parachuting into Iraq. I can hear a kettle whistling on the wood stove, three dogs snoring from their beds, a rooster crowing from the coop, and my pregnant wife and daughter breathing from our bed. A squirrel that lives in the shed has begun chirping. My brother sneaks in for coffee, pats me on the shoulder, and goes back to the yurt with a full French press. I look outside and see trees and sky, a gentle breeze blows spruce boughs and leafless birch branches. My cat tries to climb on my lap and I push her away so I can work. Two feet of snow blanket the ground, and while we wait to start working the soil hundreds of seedlings grow in our living room reminding us that life is precious and the season is here. Our beekeeping equipment is inventoried and ready, our taps await birch trees, and our solar panels are finally doing their jobs. We barely run the generator besides pumping the well, running the food processor, and toasting bread. I remove the kettle from the stove, replace it with a big pot of water to heat for dishes and bathing, and sit on a stool in the kitchen to continue writing.

How wealthy I am! To have chores and responsibilities that I enjoy and provide me with peace and purpose like never before. After all that I have been through in my life, I am finally a grateful man.

We have two big pots full of well water heating on the stove; a septic tank with a toilet, an outhouse, a tiny refrigerator, a freezer full of fish and berries, a food cache with buckets of dry goods, a propane cook stove, a legit water filter, a firm bed downstairs and a soft futon upstairs, and seven hundred square feet of safety and warmth that we call home. Life is peaceful out here—if I let it be. I never imagined life could be so slow and quiet, and I would like it.

It is nearly impossible to believe that I am the same man as the one these stories are written about; I sure don't feel like the same person on the inside. When most people find out that I am a former airborne infantryman, they don't believe it. I like it that way.

It was difficult for me to end *Warflower*. Not only to decide on an ending but to quit working on the book and move on with other projects. Writing this book provided me with a purpose when I didn't see a reason to live. It has helped me process grief, guilt, and trauma in ways I cannot express. From the first draft, written in explosive cursive from a cabin in the mountains of Costa Rica, through dozens of revisions and rejection letters, it has taken me over fifteen years to complete. Perhaps the process of revisiting these stories has freed me from the past and allowed me to live as a joyful, present, and grateful man. Who knows, I am not a freakin' psychologist, but I sure feel good with where I am today and I know that writing has a lot to do with it.

Of course, I hoped to end *Warflower* with the so-called *Hero's Return* as a positively changed man—welcomed with hugs and a small parade, he would live as a hardworking and respected man. Unfortunately, that is not the truth in my story, which is why I ended the book before returning home—before my alcoholism and depression escalated until my family recognized the signs and helped rescue me from myself. Since then, it has been a difficult and wonderful journey. Perhaps I will write those stories later, until then, I will summarize them, only for the most interested readers.

In February of 2007, my family talked me into leaving Alaska for a three-day vacation in Hawaii. I stayed three weeks, and then bought tickets to Belize that started a two-year journey traveling across Central America, where I found a spiritual practice that fits, and a love of culture, learning, and travel that does not include guns and fear. I spent six months traveling in India and Nepal, where I discovered the importance and power of forgiveness, mountains, and meditation, and where I learned that being openly spiritual outside of temples and church is a normal way of life for millions of people. I used my GI Bill to attend Central Oregon Community College in Bend, Oregon before transferring to The Evergreen State College in Olympia, Washington to focus on Sustainable Agriculture and Creative Writing; where I learned the healing power of working with plants and animals, became the first in my family to receive a college degree, and discovered the value of being around people with different lifestyles, opinions, and ideas. I worked dozens of jobs in Alaska, from a Rental Shop Attendant at a ski resort to a Busboy, a Longshoreman to a Newspaper Reporter, a Commercial Fisherman to a Laborer, a Prep Cook to a Substitute Teacher. I have battled nightmares, guilt, and depression with help from counselors, recovery rooms, friends, and family. I deal with addiction and mental health issues on a daily basis. Some days are easier than others, but every day is a good day when I don't use drugs and alcohol. I trudged through the remorse that comes from relapses until finally finding a healthy rut that has led me to over seven years clean and sober. I was diagnosed with PTSD in 2009 and provided a monthly compensation that has kept me off the streets and helped my family stay afloat when Dad isn't doing so hot. I attended technical school to learn construction skills and EMT school to hopefully save a life someday. I did all of this between the ages of 22 and 35; I guess you could say that I have been the stereotypical war veteran who returns home shell shocked and begins jumping around in search of camaraderie and purpose.

In 2012, I bought twenty acres and an unfinished house in Happy Valley, Alaska in hopes of pursuing my dream of living off the land and having a family farm. I later met, married, and work hard to stay with the woman of my dreams, Savanna Joy Stark. We have a beautiful daughter named Primrose Flora Lynn, and another child on the way. I am truly blessed. My brother currently shares the land with us, and seeing Primrose get excited every morning when her Uncle comes inside for coffee is a highlight of my day.

We have a flock of chickens that provide us with eggs and a large garden with plenty of fruits and vegetables. We sell and barter food in our community, work part-time for money and community involvement, and have close friends who love us like family. We live a relatively balanced life between being prepared for the unknown, being preppers, and enjoying the moment. I have come to see my past not as a burden but as a lesson that can be shared with others. Not to dwell but to utilize the skills I learned to make life a little better.

I was able to meet my father two separate times before he passed, one time was with my brother. I was able to spend countless hours with my mother as a sober and healthy man before she, too, passed. I cherish those moments and have come to honor both my father and mother.

I want to thank you from the bottom of my heart for reading my book and supporting me on this journey. I hope my story has touched you in some way. If so, please share it with somebody else. Never give up, no matter what battle is being fought. There is hope for all of us.

Contact me if you want to talk: Robert Stark, PO Box 986, Anchor Point, AK. 99556

ACKNOWLEDGEMENTS

I want to thank so many people for the love and support they provided throughout my life; to the exes that dealt with my craziness and their parents; the temporary friends that came and went yet left a lasting impact; my buddies I don't talk to but I think about daily; the former War Veterans who are still alive and kicking and show me that I can drive on no matter what; to Knut Hamsun, Ernest Hemingway, Michael Crichton, and John Steinbeck, for teaching, inspiring, and entertaining; to the members of my former band, Bob's Market, you guys helped me get through my mother's death in style; to Kim, my former counselor, who loved me, and hugged me, and brought me all of the fixings to make a Thanksgiving Dinner when I lived alone out in the country without any friends nearby; to my dog, Nala, who sat by my side and wept when I sat at the base of a tree with a gun ready to end my life, she kept me alive during some tough times, no doubt; to my former professors at The Evergreen State College who understood my PTSD and supported me missing class yet allowed me to turn in work that proved I was doing something during hard times when I could not bring myself to be around people; to the Veterans Affairs for providing me with a monthly stipend, I can bitch and complain all day, but the VA is doing more for my generation of veterans than any of the hard-up veterans of the past.

Thank you to the 173rd Airborne Brigade, Alpha Company 1/508, 2nd Platoon, 3rd Squad, especially John Sullivan and Jerry Brammer. You guys kept me alive. Thank you to the men I served with in the 4/101 Pathfinder Company, you were, and still are, my brothers. FILO. Thank you Thomas Whitelow, my battle buddy who stuck by my side from 173rd to 101st and continues to support me after. Thank you John Straley, for reading *Warflower* and offering all kinds of advice, both literary and non, and telling a room full of students one day that I am the most talented writer Alaska has ever seen and that I will blow Alaska out of the water in the next twenty years with my talent. Thank you mother, for being my biggest writing fan; you printed all of my blogs and journal entries and shared them with everybody you knew. Thank you to my brother, James, you read *Warflower* back when it was a harsh and mean draft that pointed a lot of fingers, and you didn't take it too personally. Thank you Fiona North, for taking time away from NYU and your family to read, edit, and offer loads of encouraging words of support. You compared my work to Tim O'Brien! Thank you Buddy North, my teammate, colleague, root. Thank you Chico Herbison, my professor, mentor, and friend who read *Warflower* and convinced me that it needed to be read by others. Thank you Martha Fleming and Jackie Marshall, back in high school you saw my potential when others didn't. Thank you Barry and Donna White, for the idea to self-publish and for the continued support you provide my family every day. Thank you to all of the agents who rejected me, you were the catalyst to return to my punk rock roots by saying F popular culture, so I published this bad boy myself.

Thank you to Savanna Joy Stark, my love, my life, my wife—you were the final reader, and the one who supports me daily. I could not have completed this journey without your consistent encouragement, love, and belief. Thank you Primrose Flora Lynn Stark, my daughter, for making me laugh, smile, and be the best me I can be while dealing with anxiety about this book. You are the future of this world, do your best.

Lastly, I want to thank God, for keeping me alive, resilient, and hopeful.

Mom and Dad had both of us kids in their early twenties. Unfortunately, their marriage did not last.

Living in Nome, Alaska as a little boy was like growing up on a huge playground. Some of the best years of my life.

I caught my first salmon right around this time, and I've been living on them ever since.

Brothers in Nome.

With my mother the day before leaving Seward, Alaska for basic training in Fort Benning, Georgia.

Right after this picture was taken I was loaded into a cattle car and taken to Airborne School. I never saw these two men again.

Days after parachuting into Northern Iraq.

Every achievement in my life has been compared to the welcome parade when we arrived in Mosul. They were ready for Saddam's rule to end, and we were there to shut him down.

The trio in Northern Iraq. John Sullivan and Jerry Brammer watched my back all day every day, I would probably be dead if not for them.

Right after we moved into Kirkuk, we began patrolling the streets on a regular basis with our faces painted.

There comes a point when searching houses, patrolling streets, running traffic control points, and enduring a war zone that you need to just lay down to take a break.

Sometimes we searched villages and arrested every male of "fighting age." We kicked in doors, woke up sleeping people in their homes with our guns in their faces, then took them off for questioning.

Detainees wait in line to enter the detainment facility.

We would return to Camp Renegade in Kirkuk from our safe houses throughout the city and surrounding villages. John Sullivan, Jerry Brammer, and the Author.

While Thomas Whitelow III was in Charlie Company 1/508th and I was in Alpha Company 1/508th, we went through basic training and airborne school together and became fast friends. We transferred from Vicenza, Italy to the 4/101 Pathfinder Company where we deployed for the second time in the same squad. From completely different walks of life, we are still friends.

We had some really good times in Iraq, especially when we could take a break from MREs and T-Rats to eat some local grub.

Jalaal was kind, gentle, and brilliant. We watched out for him like he was one of us. I often wonder about him and hope he is well.

We had a mission for weeks stacking piles of unexploded ordinances into abandoned Republican Guard vehicles that we would strap with C4 and blow up. They made for long days in the heat with one explosive payoff.

Leighton Jones could sleep through anything. One tiresome day, Jones fell asleep riding in the back of the Humvee over some very bumpy terrain with his chin resting on a stack of mines he had piled on his lap. We woke him up.

Our platoon was voted as having the worst living conditions in the military by Stars and Stripes Newspaper during this time. With extreme heat and endless patrols, we bathed in the Tigris River and slept on dirt without shade. Our only escape was this underground control bunker where a dozen guys would circle around a 4-inch DVD player to forget about reality.

After parachuting into Iraq on March 26, 2003, we left the country on February 19, 2004. The author with Jerry Brammer and John Sullivan.

After transferring to 101st Airborne Division, I worked as a Pathfinder. My second deployment in Iraq was spent as private security for the Commanding General, Major General Thomas Turner.

I couldn't pack my car to leave the military fast enough! While it's easy to join the military, it sure is difficult to get out.

Being around my mother after enduring so many experiences was ointment for my wounds. In red rock country, Sedona Arizona.

Being silent in nature has healed me more than anything else. Sitting under a tree in Sedona.

I made it to the bottom of the Grand Canyon and back up in a single day. If I were to do it again, I would take my time.

A reunion of my grandmother and mother in Nampa, Idaho. Two powerful women.

Here are my grandparents, happy in love, before my grandfather was sent to Vietnam.

Whether it was having six kids, enduring Vietnam, or a long combination of things I will never know, my grandparents do not seem to be enjoying themselves anymore. Bottom Right: Mother Sheri, Uncle Joe, Aunt Kathy. Top Right: Uncle Ronnie, Grandmother Shirley, Aunt Gwen, Uncle Don, Grandfather Joseph Moore.

I've always loved bowling. Bowling with Bruce and mother in Eugene, Oregon.

My mother spent countless hours on the telephone with her husband. Being married to Victor for thirteen years were the best years of her life.

My brother James and I reunited after years apart.

Two brothers on a wooded trail.

My brother and I at the Olympia Farmer's Market. I went
to college in Olympia and fell in love with the little city.

Our mother always wanted two sons, and no matter what we did, she was proud of us. Family photo in Seward, Alaska.

The only time I can remember my brother, father, and me together. We met at a hotel in Oregon and watched a total solar eclipse on August 21, 2017. He died shortly after.

My wife, Savanna, daughter Primrose, and me. I am a very, very lucky man. Grateful for every day that I am alive to be with them. This photo was taken on November 8, 2021.

ABOUT THE AUTHOR

Robert Stark is a lifelong Alaskan. He joined the United States Army as an airborne infantryman five days after high school and was stationed with the 173rd Airborne Brigade in Vicenza, Italy. On March 26, 2003, he parachuted into Northern Iraq during the invasion and spent 11 months patrolling Kirkuk and the surrounding areas. He returned for a second tour in 2005 as private security for the 101st Airborne Division's Commanding General. He lives off-grid with his family in Happy Valley, Alaska where they own and operate a small farm named Secret Garden Alaska.

Milton Keynes UK
Ingram Content Group UK Ltd.
UKHW020643291123
433416UK00018B/1395

Printed in the USA
CPSIA information can be obtained
at www.ICGtesting.com
CBHW070339041224
18362CB00047B/588